Nelson Mathematics 1

Activity Book

Series Authors and Senior Consultants
Marian Small • Mary Lou Kestell

Senior Author
Heather Kelleher

Grade 1 Author Team Leader
Karen LaRone

Assessment Consultants
Joanne Simmons • Damian Cooper

NELSON / EDUCATION

NELSON EDUCATION

Nelson Mathematics 1
Activity Book

Series Authors and Senior Consultants
Marian Small, Mary Lou Kestell

Senior Author
Heather Kelleher

Grade 1 Author Team Leader
Karen LaRone

Grade 2 Author Team Leader
Joanne Simmons

Authors
Linda Adams, Lynne Blake,
Karen Chong, Mary Anne Cowan,
Cheryl Cristobal, Sara Damaso,
Lalie Harcourt, Anna Jupp,
Karen LaRone, Norma MacFarlane,
Janice Novakowski, Joanne Simmons,
Marian Small, Deb Weber,
Ricki Wortzman

Assessment Consultants
Joanne Simmons, Damian Cooper

Director of Publishing
David Steele

Senior Publisher, Mathematics
Beverley Buxton

Senior Program Manager
Shirley Barrett

**First Folio Resource Group, Inc.:
Program Manager**
Fran Cohen

Senior Developmental Editor
Susan Petersiel Berg

Developmental Editors
David Bowman
Sarah Mawson
Brenda McLoughlin
Amanda Stewart

**Executive Managing Editor,
Development & Testing**
Cheryl Turner

**Executive Managing Editor,
Production**
Nicola Balfour

Senior Production Editors
Lisa Dimson
Gary Burford

Editorial Assistant
Courtney Thorne

Senior Production Coordinator
Sharon Latta Paterson

Creative Director
Angela Cluer

Art Director
Ken Phipps

Art Management
ArtPlus Ltd: Donna Guilfoyle,
Joelle Cottle; Kyle Gell

Illustrators
ArtPlus, Maryann Kovalski,
Bill Suddick, Sacha Warunkiw

Interior Design
Peggy Rhodes

Cover Design
Suzanne Peden

Cover Image
Christoph Burki/Stone/Getty Images

Composition
Kyle Gell Design

Printer
Globus

**National Library of Canada
Cataloguing in Publication**

Nelson elementary mathematics.
Grade one workbook / Marian
Small ... [et al].

ISBN 0-17-626083-8

1. Mathematics—Problems,
exercises, etc. I. Small, Marian

QA107.2.N44 2004
510   C2004-901401-3

Contents

Write About Math

Draw something that belongs in each group.

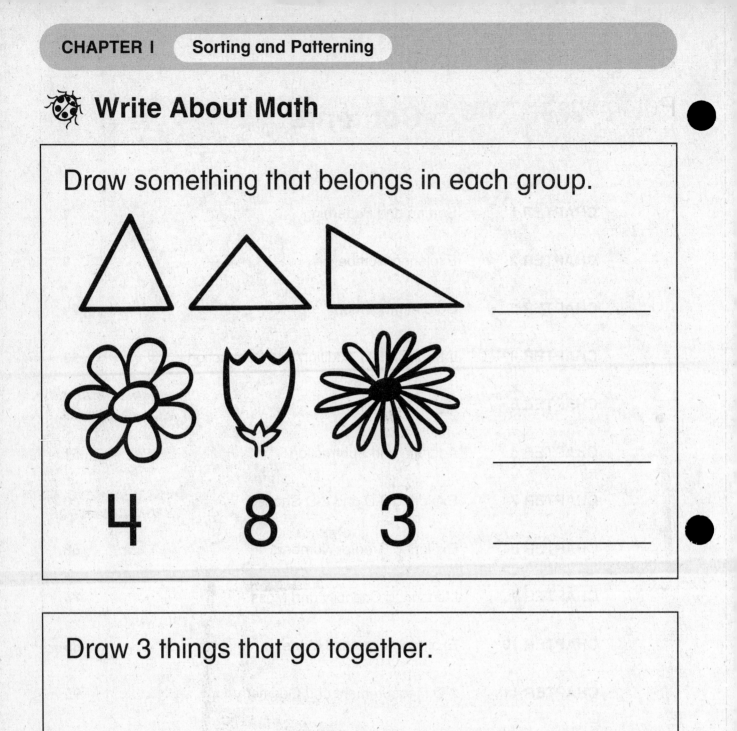

Draw 3 things that go together.

These things go together because

Backpack Sorting Mat

Put things that are alike in the same pockets.

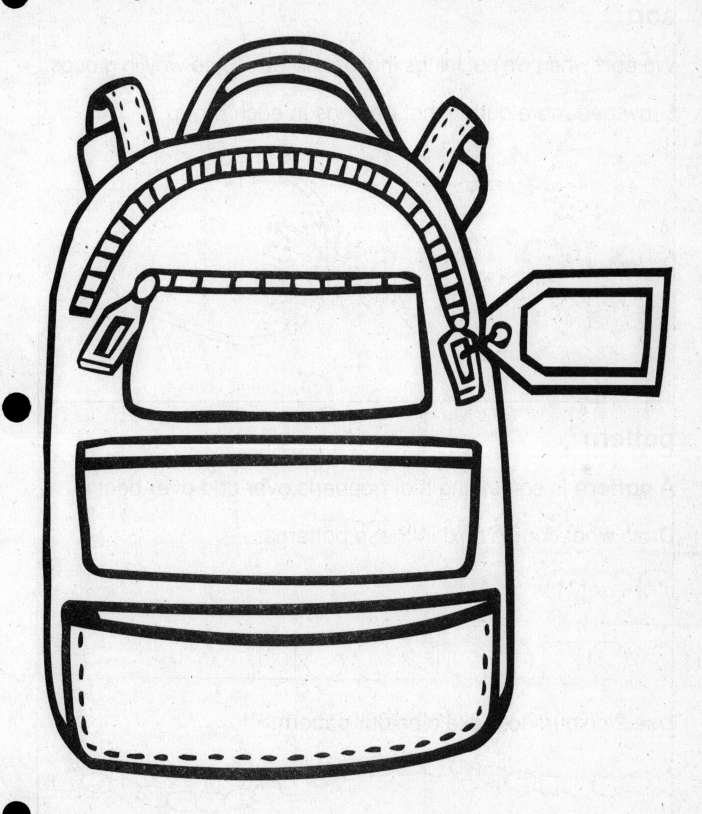

Glossary Words

sort

We **sort** when we put things that are alike in some way in groups.

Draw one more button that belongs in each group.

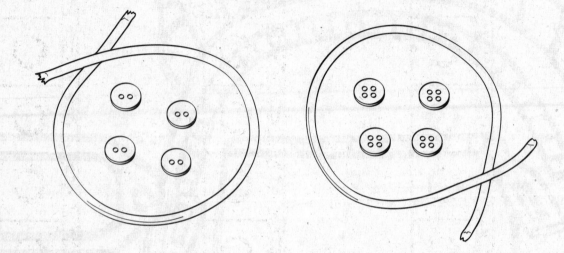

pattern

A **pattern** is something that happens over and over again.

Draw what comes next in these patterns.

☺ ♡ ☺ ♡ ☺ ♡ ___ ___

◯ ◯ ☐ ◯ ◯ ☐ ◯ ◯ ☐ ___ ___ ___ ___

Use 2 colours to make a colour pattern.

Cube Trains

Train ___

Train ___

Train ___

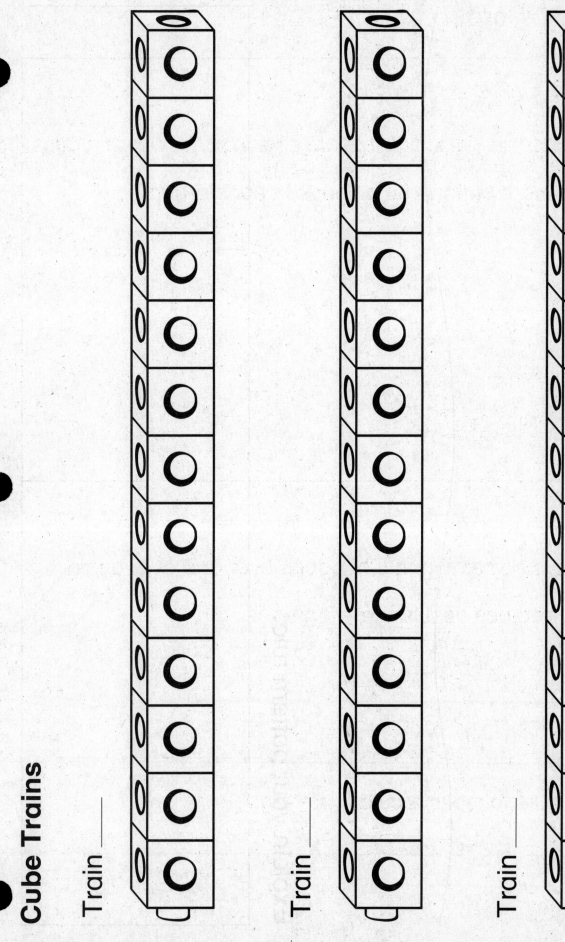

Chapter 1 Lesson 4

Activity 1.4

Necklace Patterns

Draw your pattern.

Explain your pattern rule.

Parade Paths

Draw a different pattern on each path.
Describe each pattern using letters, words, or numbers.

Path 1

Pattern Sentence 1 _____

Path 2

Pattern Sentence 2 _____

A pattern can look like this:

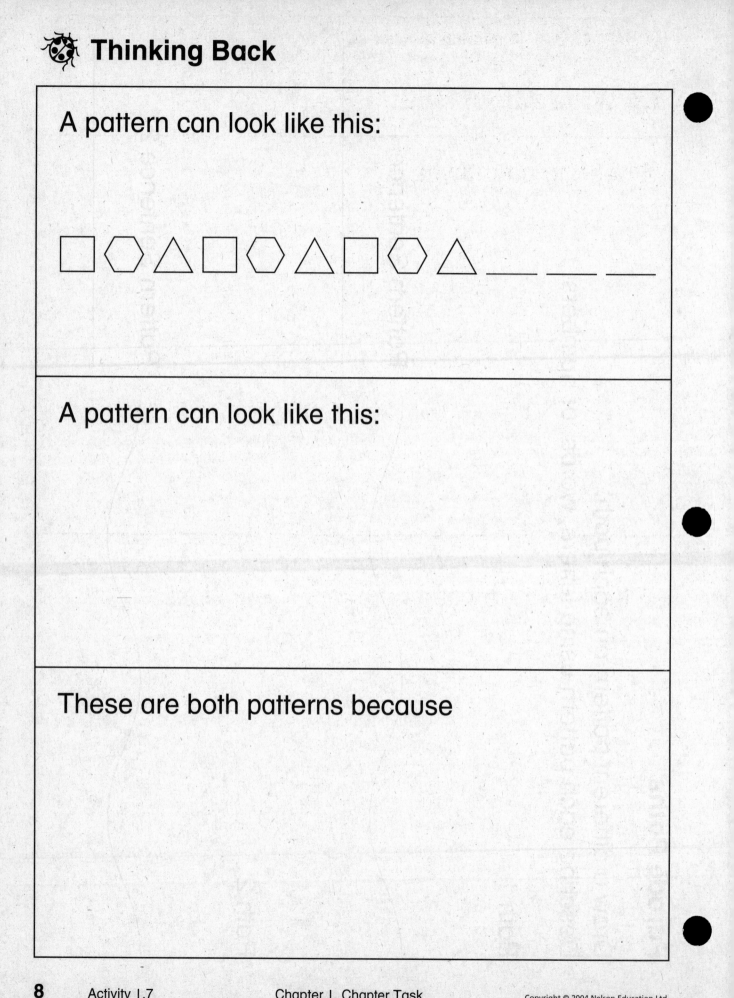

A pattern can look like this:

These are both patterns because

Write About Math

I need to count when

Places where I see numbers in our classroom:

Tile Designs

Circle the design that uses more tiles.

Name _____ My Design

I used ____ tiles.

Name _____ My Design

I used ____ tiles.

Letters in My Name

● My name is _____.

How many letters are in your name? Colour cubes to show the number.

> My name has _____ letters.
>
> _____ letters is _____ than 5.
>
> _____ letters is _____ than 10.

● My friend's name is _____.

How many letters are in your friend's name? Colour cubes to show the number.

> My friend's name has _____ letters.
>
> _____ letters is _____ than 5.
>
> _____ letters is _____ than 10.

What's Missing?

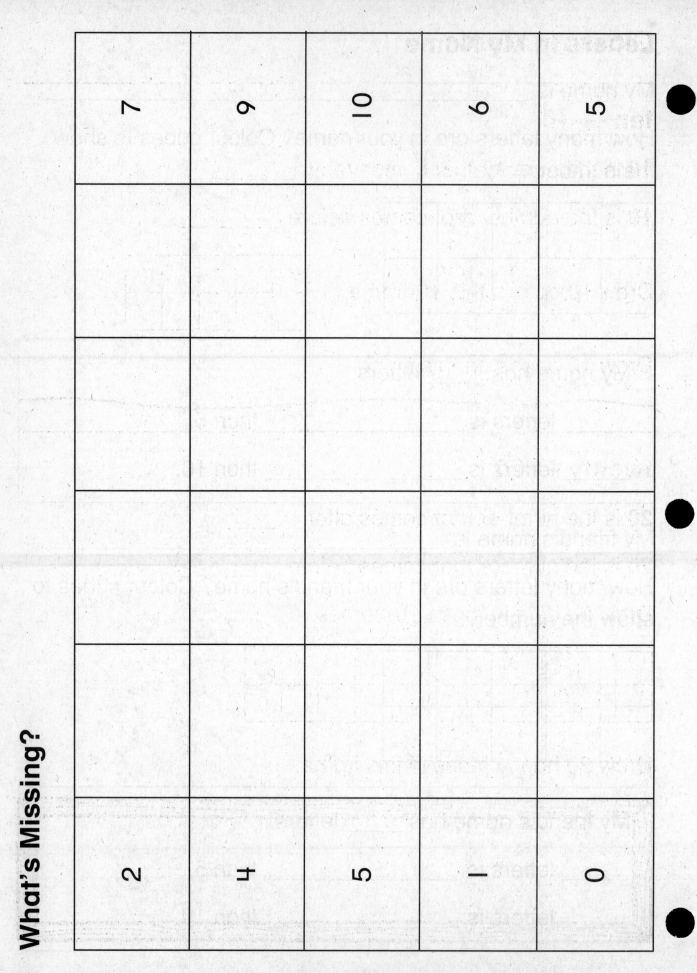

7				2
9				4
10				5
6				1
5				0

Glossary Words

ten — 10

10 is the number that comes after _____.

10 is the number that comes before _____.

Draw 10 dots in this 10-frame.

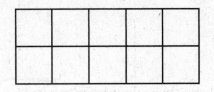

Draw 10 beads on this string.

twenty — 20

20 is the number that comes after _____.

20 is the number that comes before _____.

Draw 20 dots in these 10-frames.

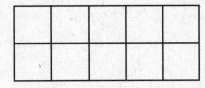

Draw 20 happy faces in this frame.

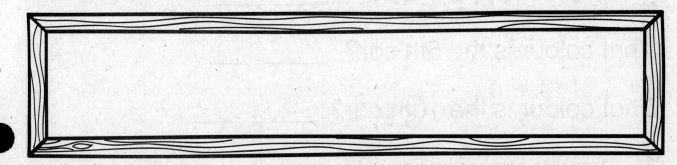

The Train Game

Colour the train you made.

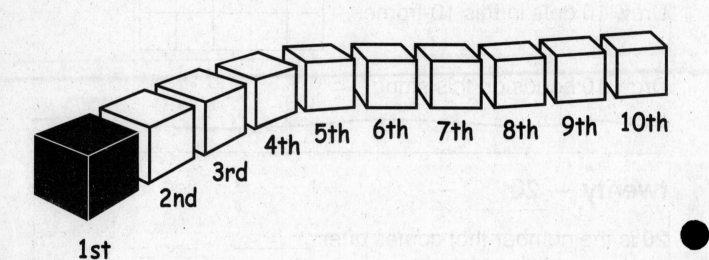

1st 2nd 3rd 4th 5th 6th 7th 8th 9th 10th

What colour is the 3rd car? _____

What colour is the 5th car? _____

What colour is the 10th car? _____

Chapter 2 Lesson 5

Two Double 10-Frames

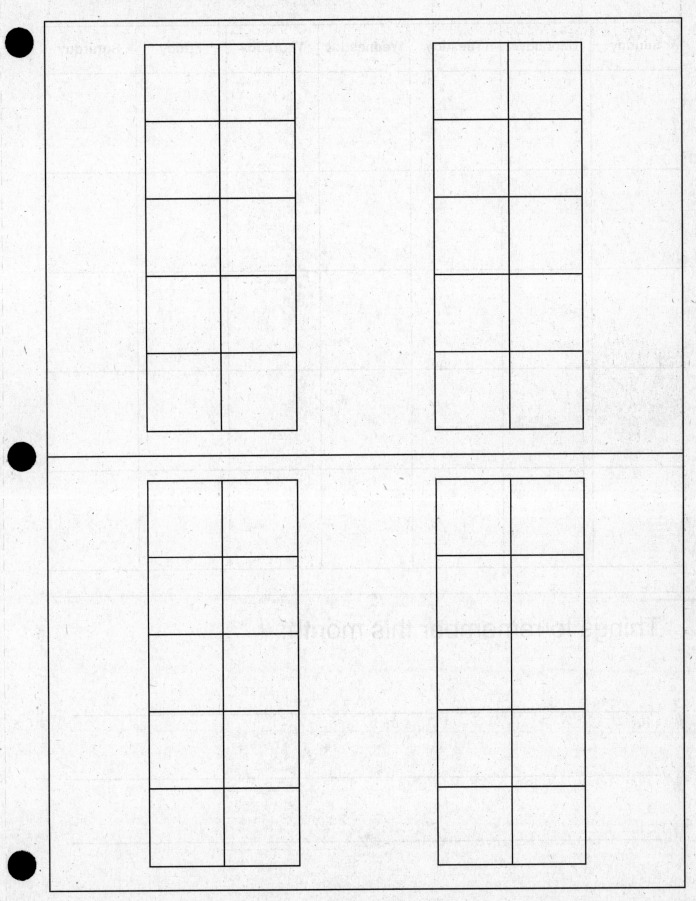

My Calendar

Sunday	Monday	Tuesday	Wednesday	Thursday	Friday	Saturday

Things to remember this month:

_____

_____

_____

Triple 10-Frame

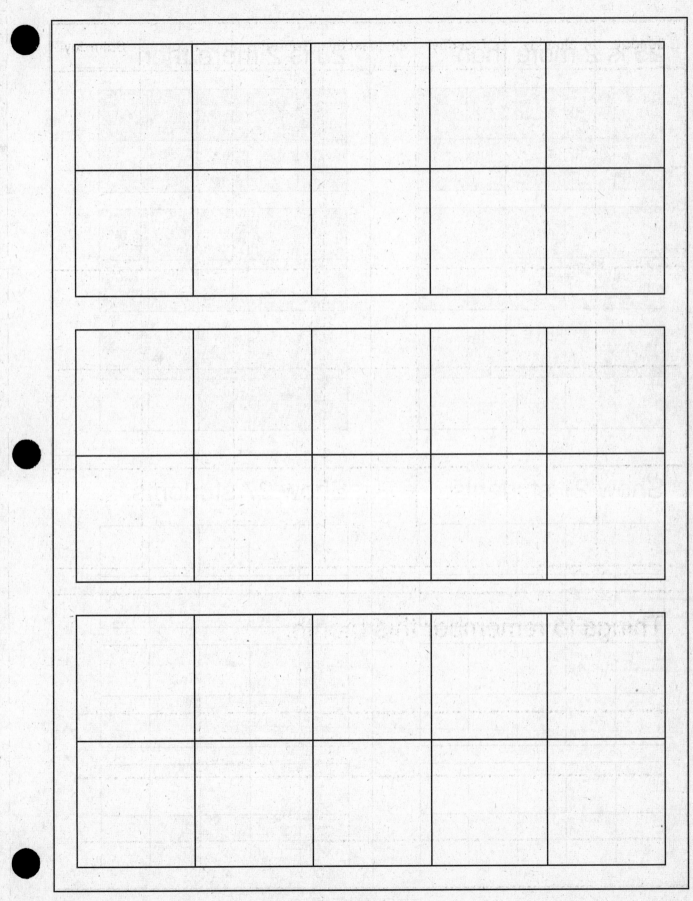

Chapter 2 Lesson 9 Activity 2.9

How Many Students?

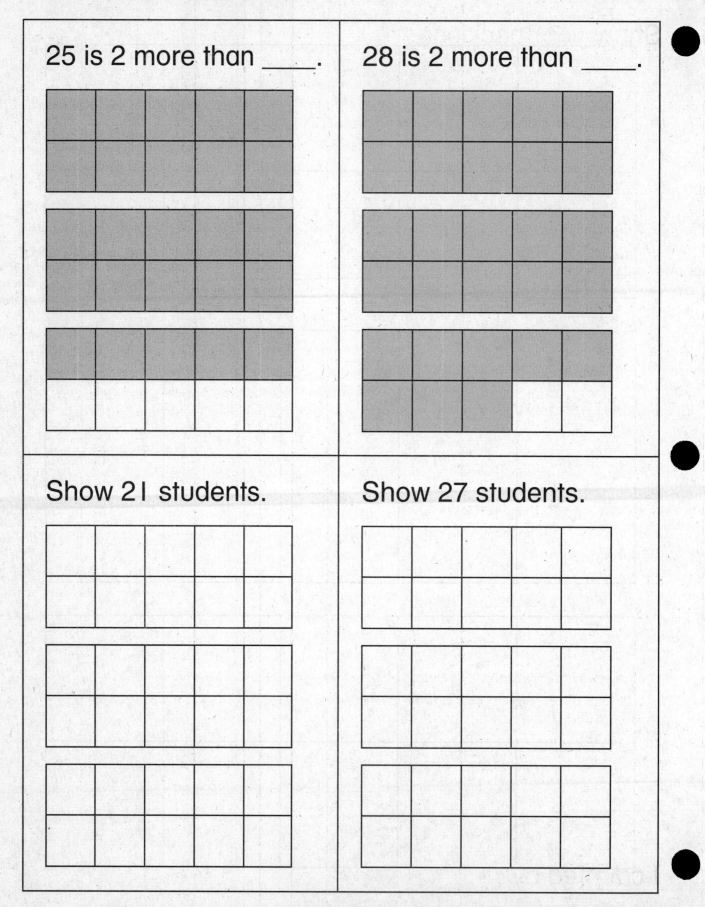

25 is 2 more than ____.

28 is 2 more than ____.

Show 21 students.

Show 27 students.

Activity 2.10   Chapter 2 Lesson 9

Ways to Count to 30

- Show your necklace.

I counted by _____.

- Show your necklace.

I counted by _____.

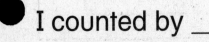

Glossary Words

thirty — 30

30 is the number that comes after _____.

30 is the number that comes before _____.

Draw 30 dots in these 10-frames.

Draw 30 dots on this scarf.

The Button Problem

1. How many buttons did Nana sew on? _____

This is how I figured it out:

2. Are there more buttons on the clothes or in the box?

Show how you know.

I used
- ☐ pictures
- ☐ numbers
- ☐ words

Squirrel's Birthday

The squirrel will have _____ nuts on the 10th day.

This is how I solved the problem:

I used
☐ pictures
☐ numbers
☐ words

Chapter 2 Chapter Task

🐞 Thinking Back

My favourite number is _____ .
Here is a picture showing my favourite number.

I know lots of ways to count.
One way I can count is like this:

Write About Math

Something I know about the children in my class is

A question I have about the children in my class is

Sort and Graph

⬤ My Title: _____

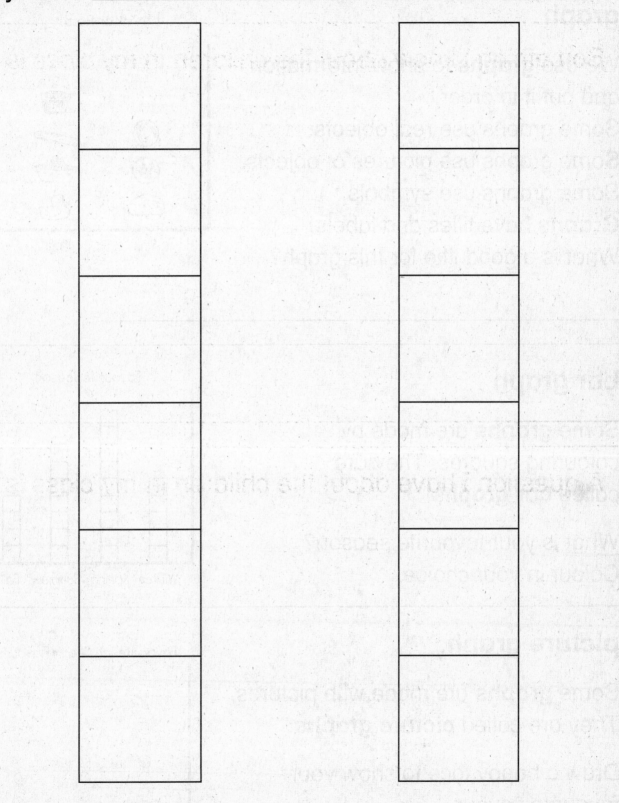

_____   _____

Glossary Words

graph

We use **graphs** to show information and put it in order.
Some graphs use real objects.
Some graphs use pictures of objects.
Some graphs use symbols.
Graphs have titles and labels.
What is a good title for this graph?

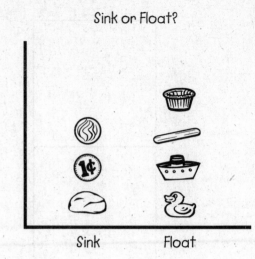

Sink or Float?

Sink   Float

bar graph

Some **graphs** are made by colouring squares. They are called **bar graphs**.

What is your favourite season?
Colour in your choice.

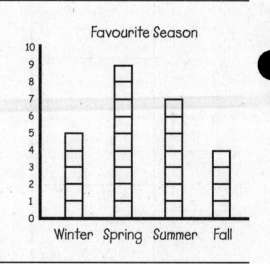

Favourite Season

picture graph

Some **graphs** are made with pictures. They are called **picture graphs**.

Draw a happy face to show your favourite flavour.

Favourite Ice Cream Flavours

Vanilla   Chocolate   Strawberry

Chapter 3 Lessons 1, 2, and 3

My Picture Graph

Title: _____

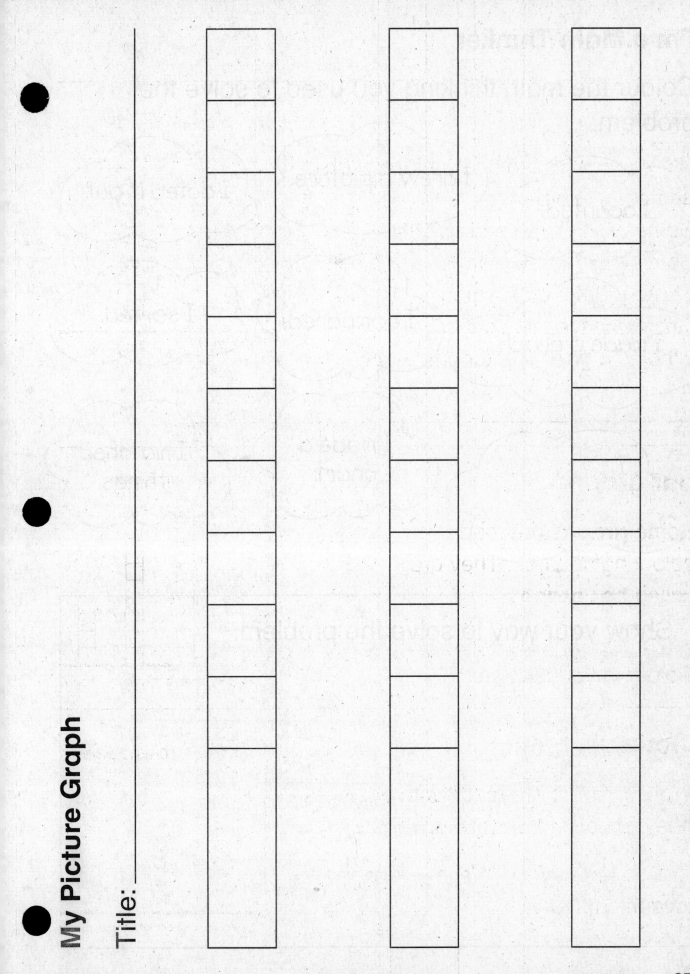

I'm a Math Thinker

Colour the math thinking you used to solve the problem.

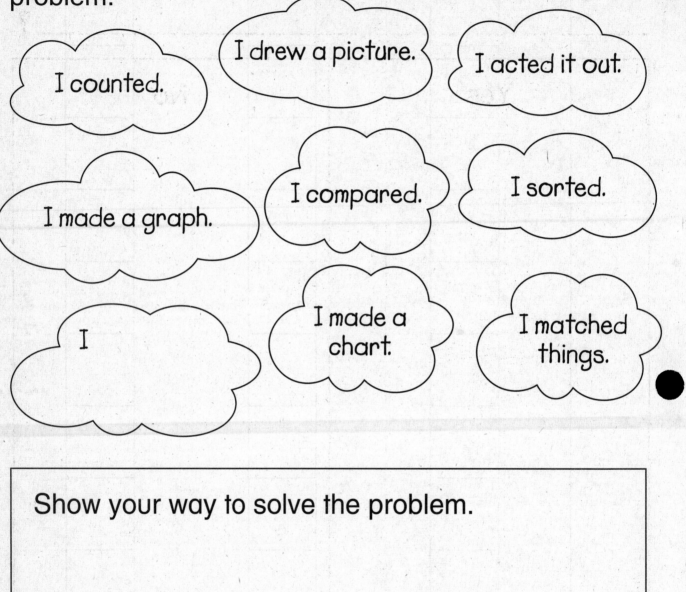

I counted.

I drew a picture.

I acted it out.

I made a graph.

I compared.

I sorted.

I

I made a chart.

I matched things.

Show your way to solve the problem.

Yes/No Tally Sheet

⬤ My question is: _____

_____ ?

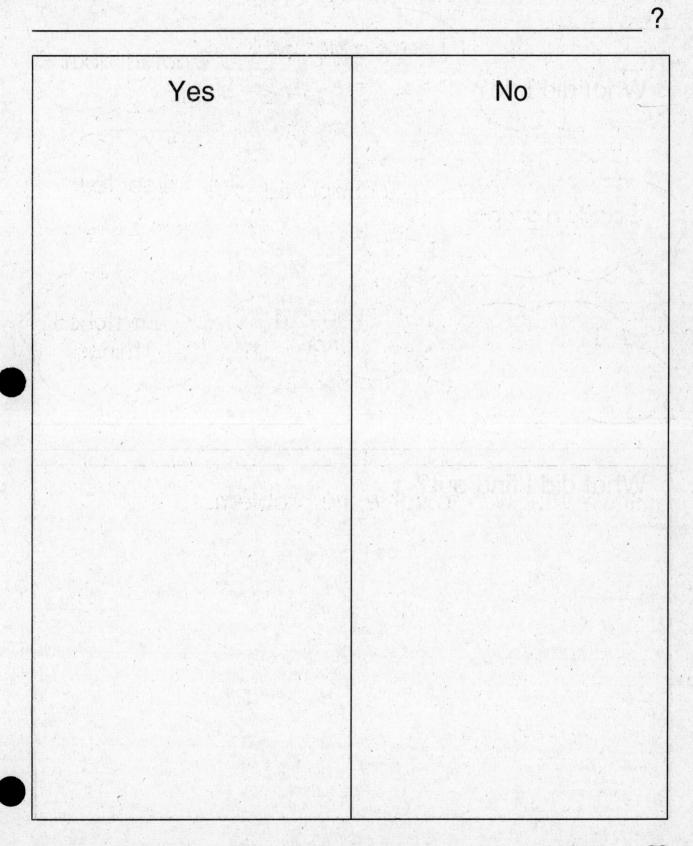

Yes	No

My Survey

My survey question is: _____

_____ ?

What did I do?

What did I find out?

Survey Recording Sheet

● My question is: _____

_____ ?

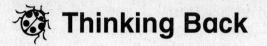 **Thinking Back**

I think graphs and surveys are useful because

A question I have about graphs or surveys is

Write About Math

Draw a story on this pond mat.

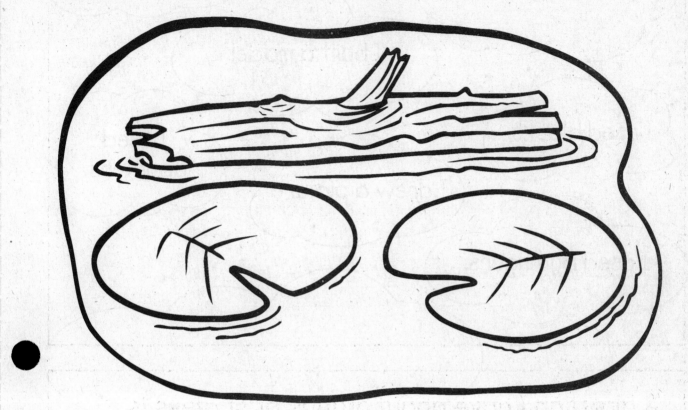

Use numbers and words to tell your story.

_____

_____

_____

_____

_____

I'm a Math Thinker

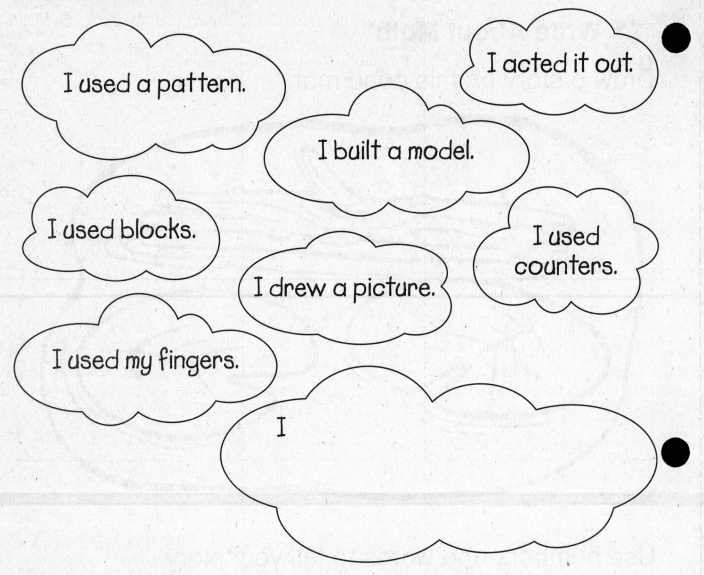

I used a pattern.

I acted it out.

I built a model.

I used blocks.

I used counters.

I drew a picture.

I used my fingers.

I

Show your way to solve the problem.

Chapter 4 Lesson 2

Glossary Words

add

We **add** to find out how many in all.
Sometimes one group joins another group.

_____ + _____
There are _____ frogs in all.

Sometimes there are two groups.

_____ + _____
There are _____ frogs in all.

subtract

We **subtract** to find out how many are left.

5 − _____
There are _____ left on the log.

We also **subtract** to compare numbers. Sometimes we **subtract** to find the missing number or parts.

Names For ____

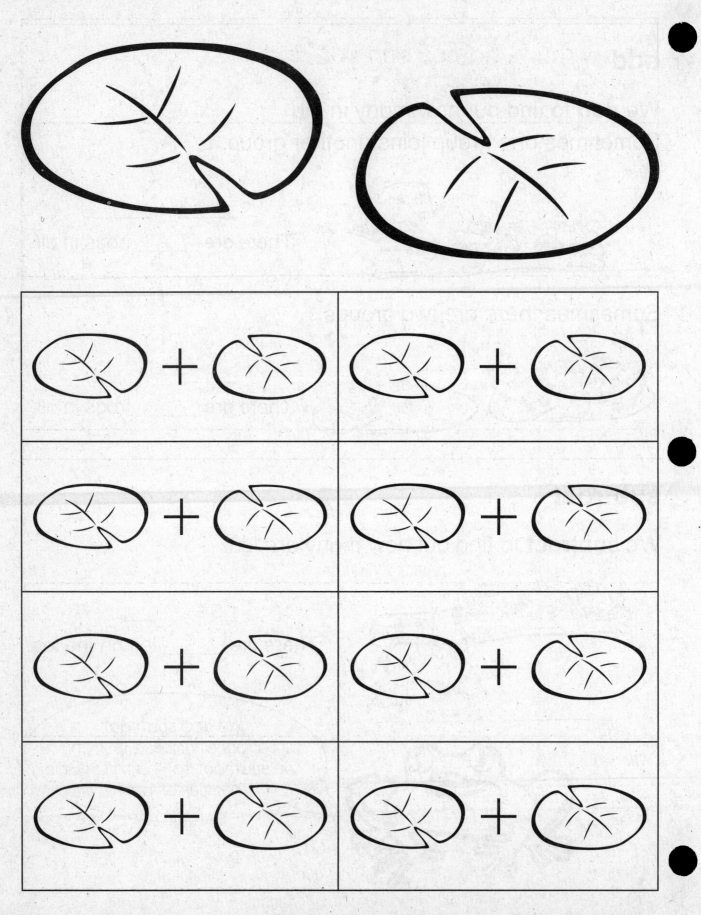

Names for Numbers 1 to 5

How many names can you find for these numbers?	
1 one	
2 two	
3 three	
4 four	
5 five	

Names for Numbers 6 to 10

How many names can you find for these numbers?	
6 six	
7 seven	
8 eight	
9 nine	
10 ten	

My Addition Story

● The title is _____

_____ + _____

Here is a picture of my story.

My story ends with the number _____.

My Subtraction Story

The title is _____

_____ – _____

Here is a picture of my story.

My story ends with the number ____.

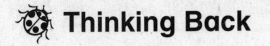 **Thinking Back**

Sometimes I add.
Draw a picture and tell about adding.

+

Sometimes I subtract.
Draw a picture and tell about subtracting.

—

🐞 Write About Math

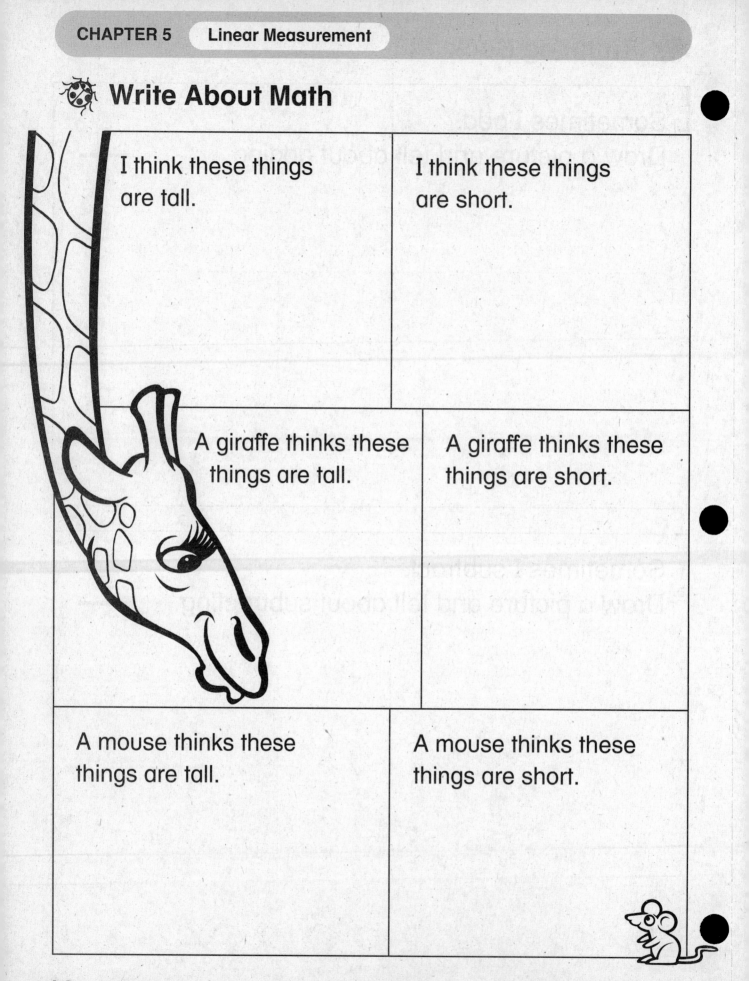

I think these things are tall.

I think these things are short.

A giraffe thinks these things are tall.

A giraffe thinks these things are short.

A mouse thinks these things are tall.

A mouse thinks these things are short.

My Footprint

I used my footprint to compare lengths.
Here is what I found.

Shorter than my foot	As long as my foot	Longer than my foot

Glossary Words

length

We can measure to compare the **length** of two things.
The pen is longer than the chalk.
The chalk is shorter than the pen.

longer

shorter

Draw a line shorter than this line.

_____

Draw a line longer than this line.

_____

We can compare the **length** of more than two things.
Here the pencil is the longest thing.
The crayon is the shortest thing.

longest

shortest

Measuring Around

Shorter than my string	As long as my string	Longer than my string

Chapter 5 Lesson 2

Activity 5.4

Snap Cube Measuring

What I Measured	My Estimate	My Measurement
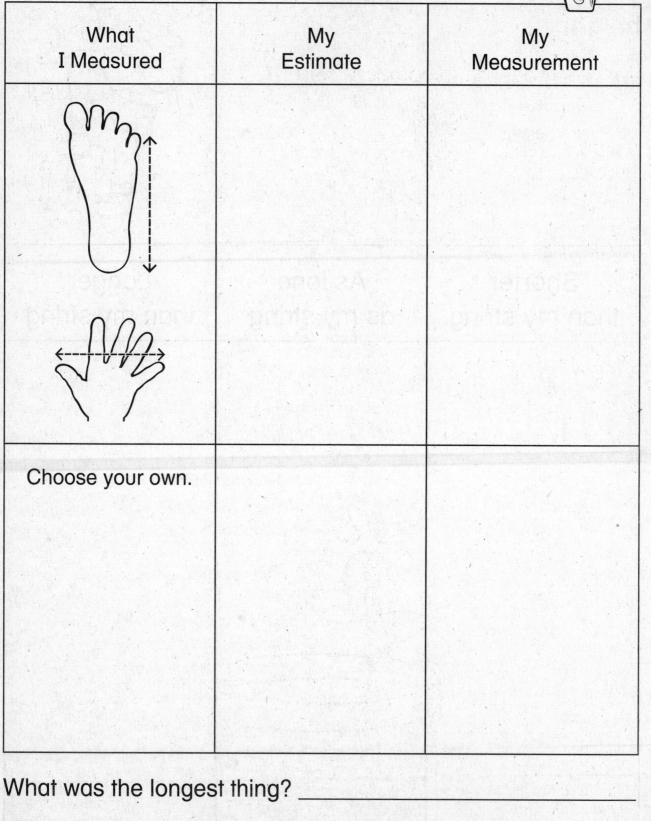		
Choose your own.		

What was the longest thing? _____

What was the shortest thing? _____

Chapter 5 Lesson 3

Glossary Words

height

We can measure to compare **height**.

Draw a taller flower.

Measuring Things

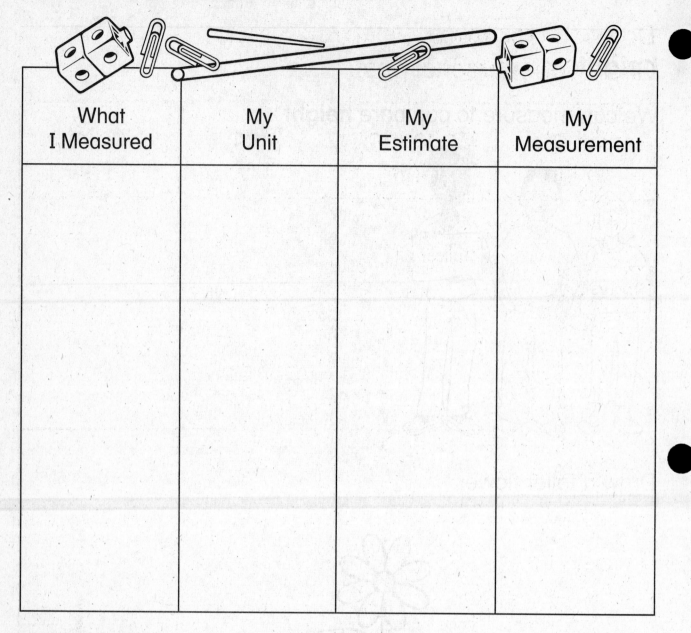

What I Measured	My Unit	My Estimate	My Measurement

My Riddle

I measured _____.

It is _____ units long.

What unit did I use?

My Personal Bests

Do each task twice.
Circle your personal best.

What to Do	Measuring Unit	First Try	Second Try

🐞 Thinking Back

What can you use to measure how long or tall things are?

How would you measure how tall you are? Use pictures, words, or numbers to show how you would measure.

Chapter 5 Chapter Task

🐞 Write About Math

My favourite subtracting song was

I like it best because

You can subtract when things fall because

Glossary Words

addition number sentence

We can use numbers and symbols
to tell about **addition**.

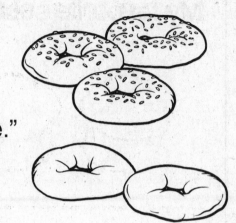

We can write 3 + 2 = 5.
We read it as "three plus two equals five."

plus
↓
3 + 2 = 5 ← sum
↑
equals

Finish these **addition number sentences**.

5 + 3 = _____   3 + _____ = 5   _____ + _____ = 4

subtraction number sentence

We can use numbers and symbols
to tell about **subtraction**.

We can write 6 − 2 = 4.
We read it as "six minus two equals four."

minus
↓
6 − 2 = 4 ← difference
↑
equals

Finish these **subtraction number sentences**.

5 − 3 = _____   6 − _____ = 5   _____ − _____ = 2

Cupcakes

● A baker had 10 candies to decorate 2 cupcakes.
Show some ways to decorate the cupcakes.
Write a number sentence to go with each picture.

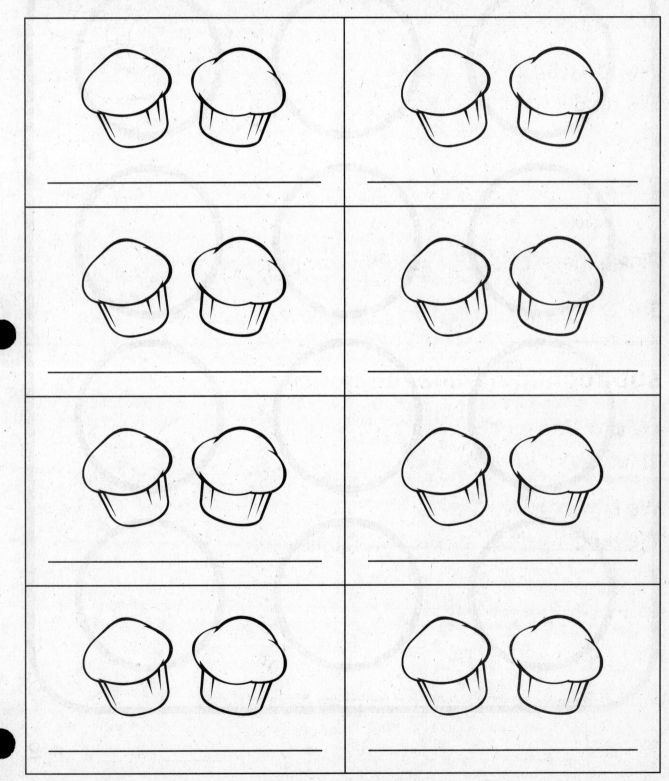

Muffin Tin Mat

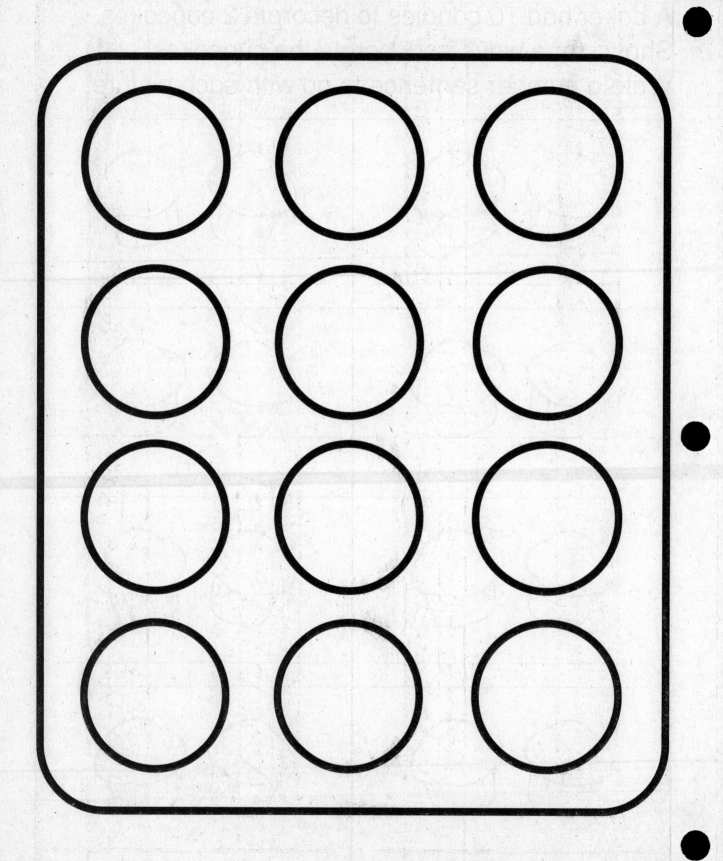

Equal Towers

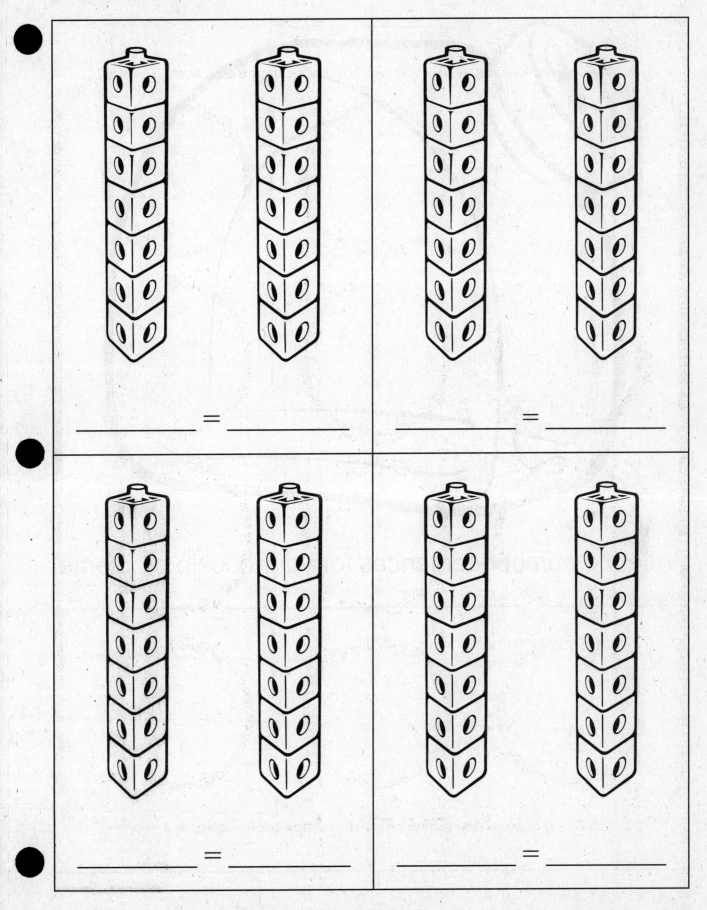

_____ = _____   _____ = _____

_____ = _____   _____ = _____

Chapter 6 Lesson 5   Activity 6.5

Cookie Jar

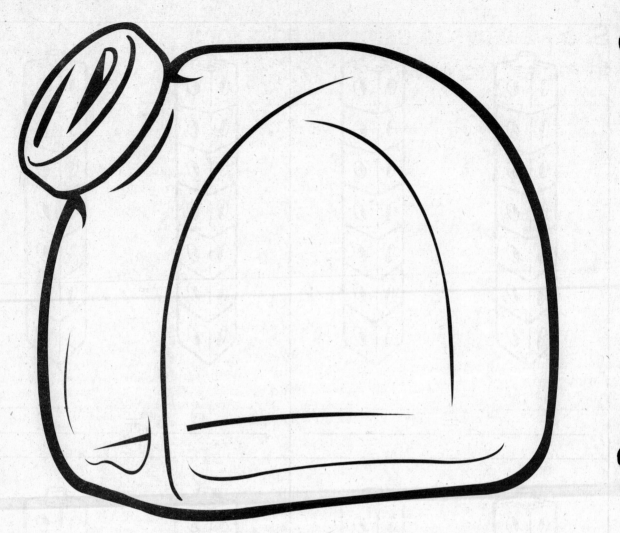

Write the number sentences for your cookie problems.

Chapter 6 Lesson 6

Calculator Names

● Show 2 ways to use your calculator to make each number.

6	7

11	12

Here is a puzzle I gave my partner:

I started with _____.

I ended with _____.

10-Frame Buses

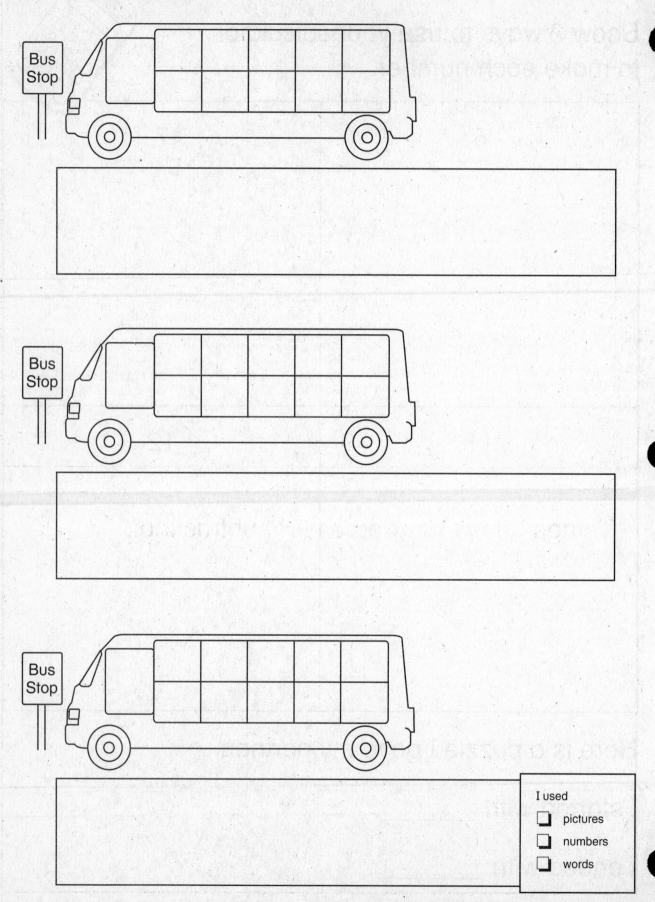

Bus Stop

Bus Stop

Bus Stop

I used

☐ pictures

☐ numbers

☐ words

Chapter 6 Chapter Task

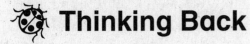

Thinking Back

Use pictures, numbers, and words.

Things I have learned about adding:

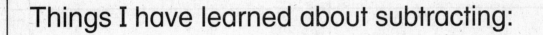

Things I have learned about subtracting:

Chapter 6 Chapter Task

Write About Math

What does it look like?
Make each shape look like something real.

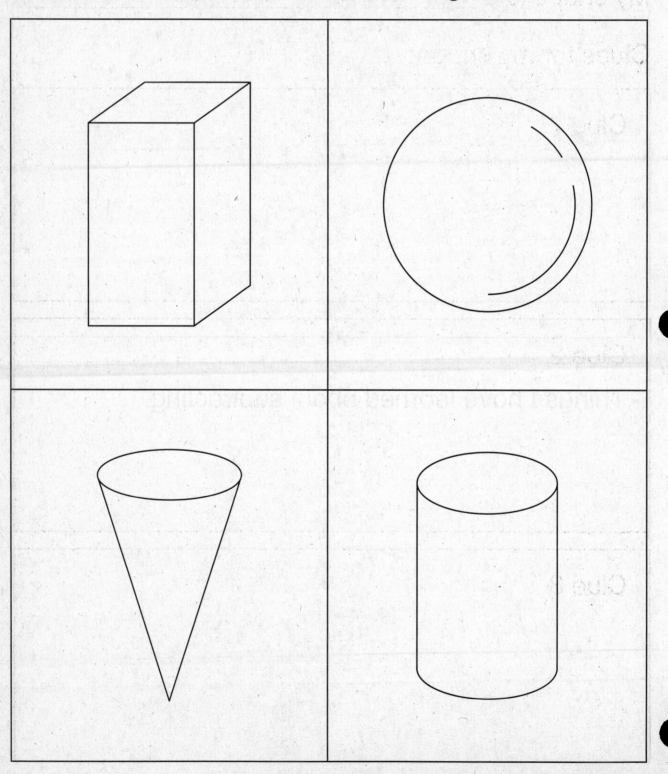

Chapter 7 Jump In

Describing Shapes

Use words, numbers, or pictures to tell about your shape.

My shape is a _____.

Clues for my shape:

Clue 1

Clue 2

Clue 3

Glossary Words

three-dimensional (3-D) shapes

These are some **three-dimensional shapes**.
We also call them **3-D shapes** or **solid shapes**.

Match the 3-D shape with the object.

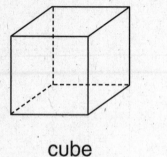  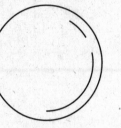 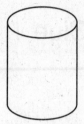

cube   cone   sphere   cylinder

Flat 3-D shapes have faces, edges, and corners.

This is
a **corner.**

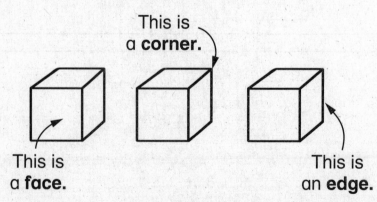

This is
a **face.**

This is
an **edge.**

Building with Shapes

● I built a _____ .

This is what it looks like.

● How many did you use?

_____ cubes 	_____ cylinders
_____ cones	_____ spheres
_____ prisms	_____ other shapes

Glossary Words

two-dimensional (2-D) shapes

These are some **two-dimensional shapes**.
When a shape is flat we call it a two-dimensional shape.

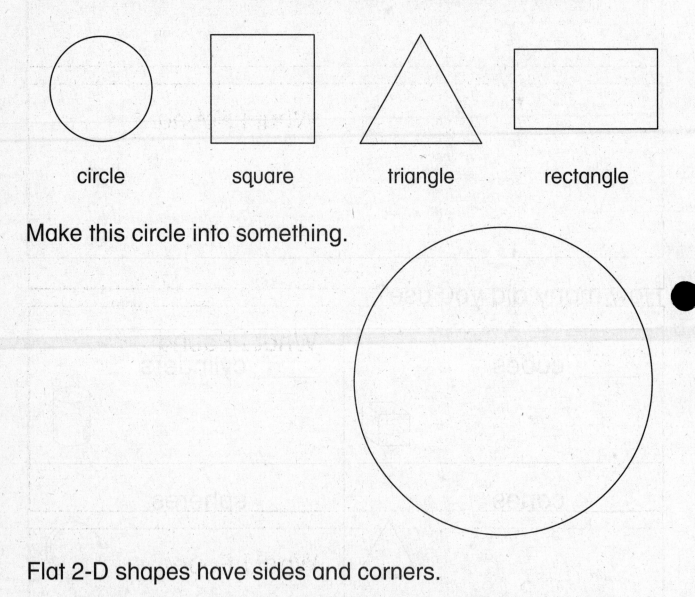

circle   square   triangle   rectangle

Make this circle into something.

Flat 2-D shapes have sides and corners.

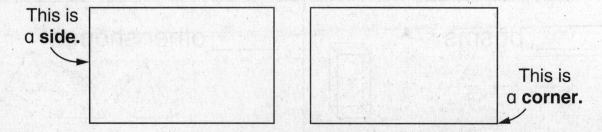

This is
a **side**.

This is
a **corner**.

I Spy

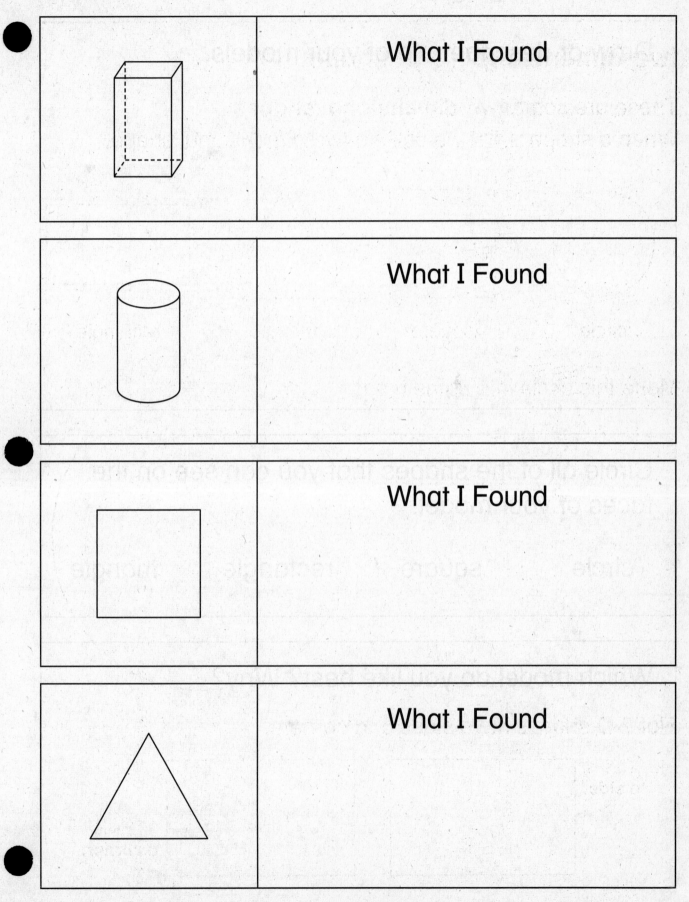

	What I Found
	What I Found
	What I Found
	What I Found

Model Display Card

Draw or describe one of your models.

Circle all of the shapes that you can see on the faces of your model.

circle   square   rectangle   triangle

Which model do you like best? Why?

🐞 Thinking Back

⬤ Choose a shape.

My shape's name is _____.

What does it look like?

Why is it interesting?

Where do you see it at school?

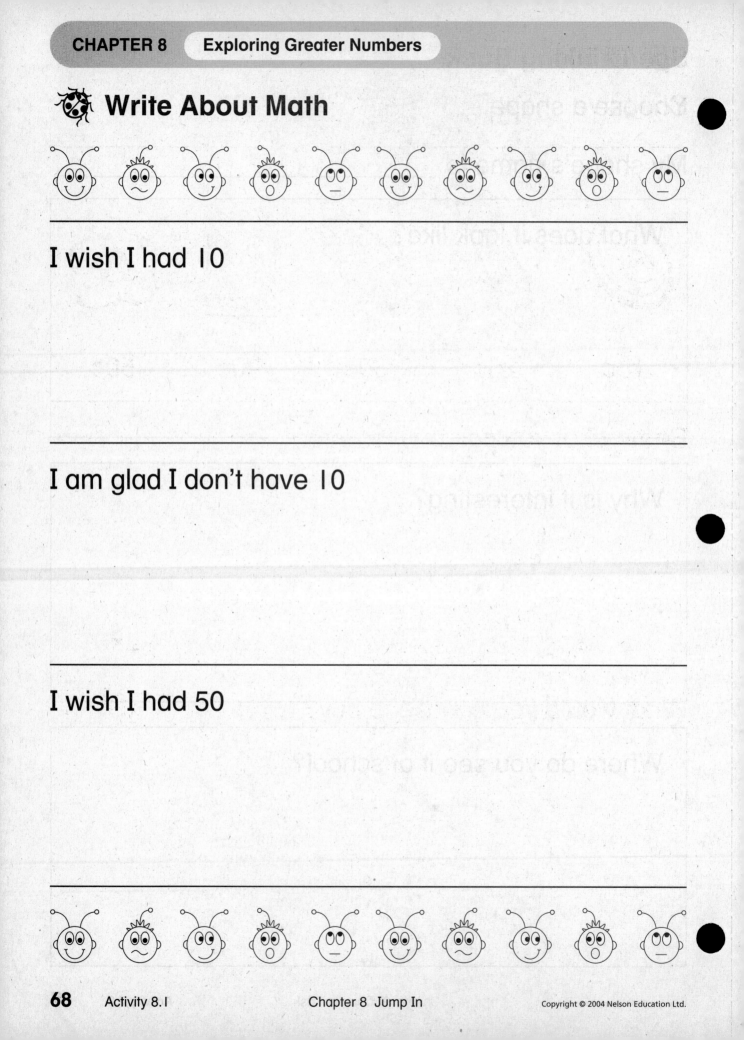

Write About Math

I wish I had 10

_____

I am glad I don't have 10

_____

I wish I had 50

_____

Spend 50¢

You have 🪙 🪙 🪙 🪙 🪙

| 10¢ | 20¢ | 30¢ | 40¢ | 50¢ |

Show what you can buy for 50¢.

What would you choose to buy?

Glossary Words

dime

A **dime** is a coin worth 10¢.

You can trade _____ pennies for _____ dime.

one dime = _____ ¢

one hundred — 100

There are 10 groups of 10 in **100**.

The number before **100** is _____ .

Try to draw 100 dots in this square.

100 Robos

● Use 2 colours.

How many ways can you make 100?

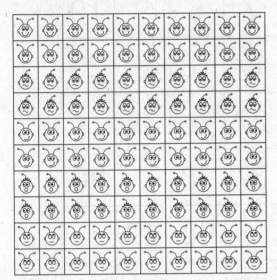

_____ and _____ is __100__ .

_____ and _____ is _____ .

_____ and _____ is _____ .

Missing Numbers

Print the missing numbers.

1	2	3	4	5	6	7	8	9	10
11	12			15		17	18		20
21		23	24		26	27		29	
31	32		34	35		37	38		40
41		43		45	46		48	49	
51	52		54			57			60
61		63		65		67	68	69	70
	72	73		75		77			80
81			84		86	87		89	90
91	92	93	94	95	96		98	99	

Think of numbers that are the same in some way.
Print the numbers here.

Chapter 8 Lesson 5

Silly Stuff for Sale

● What do these things cost?

● Draw 2 things you want to buy.
Show the dimes and pennies you need for **each one**.

How Many Cars?

Our class is going to the fair. Each person brings a friend.

How many people are going to the fair? _____

This is how I figured it out:

How many roller coaster cars do we need? _____

This is how I figured it out:

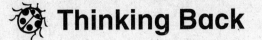

Choose a number between 30 and 50.
Draw that many happy faces.

Circle groups so it is easy to count.
Tell how you can count the groups.

Write About Math

I think that the _____ holds more because

_____

_____

_____

_____ .

I think that the _____ is heavier because

_____

_____

_____

_____ .

Glossary Words

capacity

Capacity means how much something holds.
We fill things to find out how much they can hold.

holds more   holds less

Circle the glass that is full.

Chapter 9 Lesson I   Activity 9.2   **77**

How Many to Fill?

When I filled with…	It took this many

How Many in a Handful?

● Record your estimate and your count.

What's in the Bag?	My Estimate	My Count
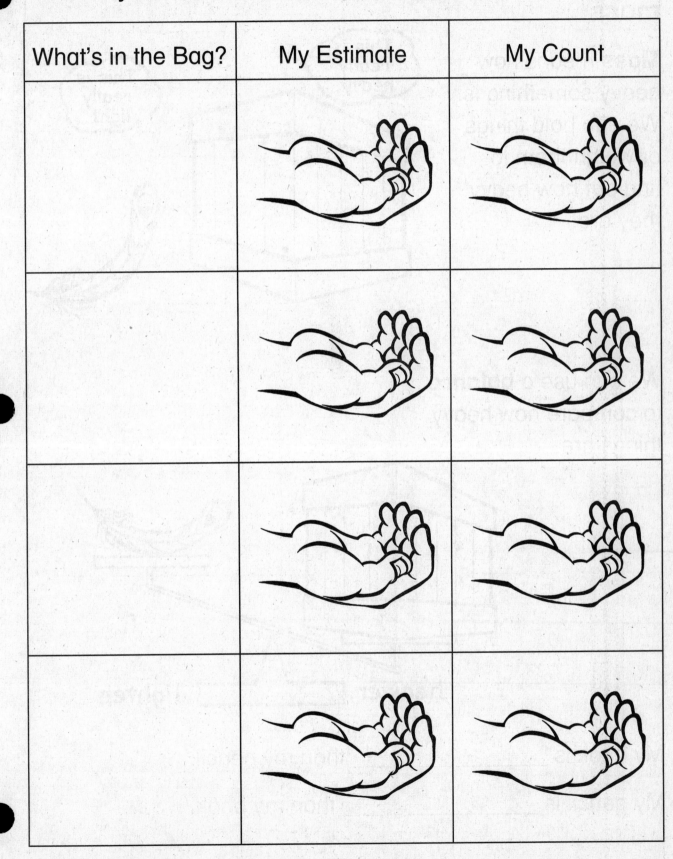		

Glossary Words

mass

Mass means how heavy something is. We can hold things or weigh them to find out how heavy they are.

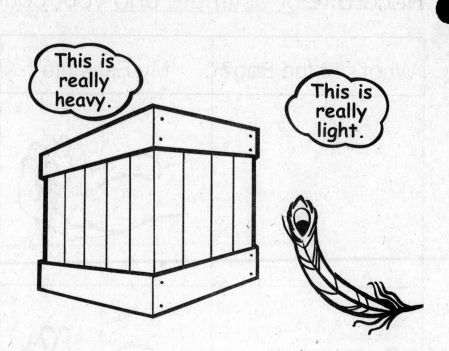

We can use a **balance** to compare how heavy things are.

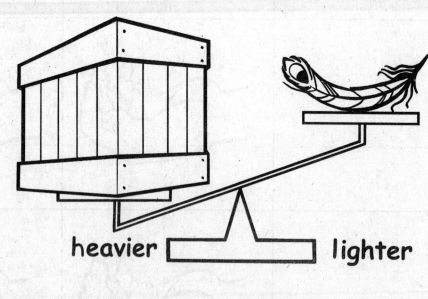

My book is _____ than my pencil.

My pencil is _____ than my book.

Estimating and Measuring Mass

● Mass of a _____

My Estimate	My Measurement

Glossary Words

half

2 equal parts of a whole are called **halves**. Each of the parts is one **half**.

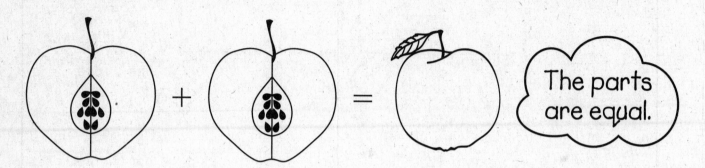

Circle the food that is cut in half.

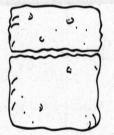

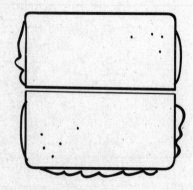

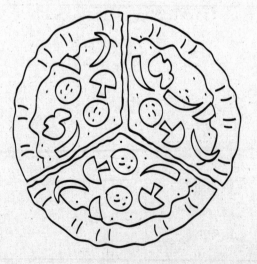

Chapter 9 Lesson 6

How Much Do They Cost?

● Here are my pictures of my packages.

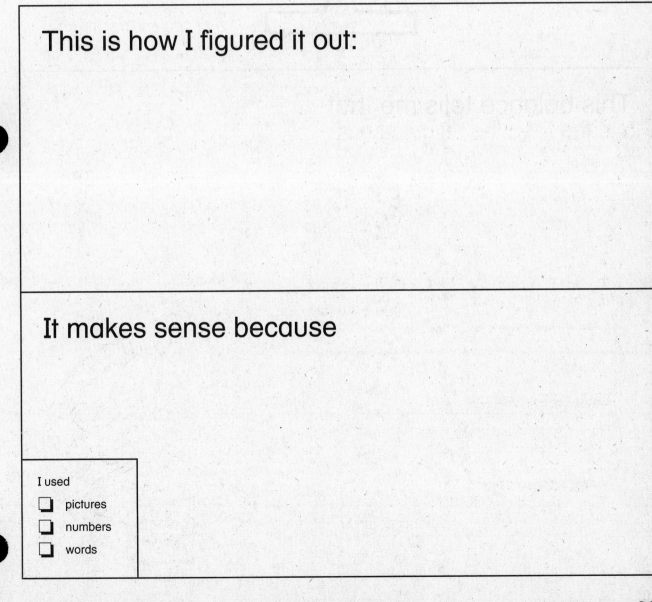

This is how I figured it out:

It makes sense because

I used
- ☐ pictures
- ☐ numbers
- ☐ words

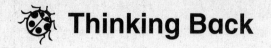

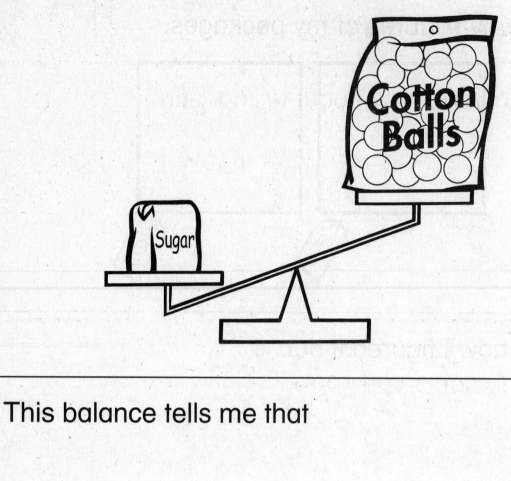

This balance tells me that

Write About Math

What do you know about telling time?

Draw the coins you know.

Draw the coin that is worth the most.

Glossary Words

month

There are 12 **months** in one **year**.
A calendar helps to measure time.
A calendar shows the year in
months, **weeks**, and **days**.

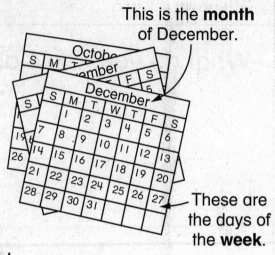

This is the **month** of December.

These are the days of the **week**.

There are _____ days in a week.

There are _____ days in the month of December.

season

There are four **seasons** in a year.
The seasons are **winter**, **spring**, **summer**, **fall**.

winter **spring** **summer** **fall**

What is your favourite season? _____

How Long Does It Take?

Less time than the ABC song	About the same time as the ABC song	More time than the ABC song

What Am I Doing?

It is _____ o'clock.

I am _____

_____.

It is _____ o'clock.

I am _____

_____.

It is _____ o'clock.

I am _____

_____.

Glossary Words

hour

There are 24 **hours** in one **day**.
There are 60 **minutes** in one **hour**.

We use a **clock** to measure time.
This clock has the numbers 1 to 12.
It has a **minute hand** and an **hour hand**.

Fill in the missing numbers.

This clock says it is _____ o'clock.

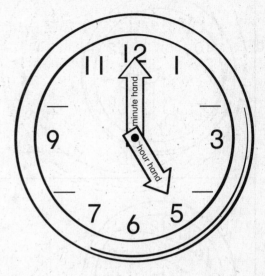

money

We use **money** to buy things.
Here are the **coins** we can use.

	penny	1 cent	_____ ¢
	nickel	5 cents	_____ ¢
	dime	10 cents	_____ ¢
	quarter	25 cents	_____ ¢

Telling Time to the Half-Hour

Write the time that each clock shows.

_____ : _____

_____ : _____

_____ : _____

_____ : _____

_____ : _____

_____ : _____

_____ : _____

_____ : _____

Counting Coins

How many cents?　　　　　　　　**Show another way.**

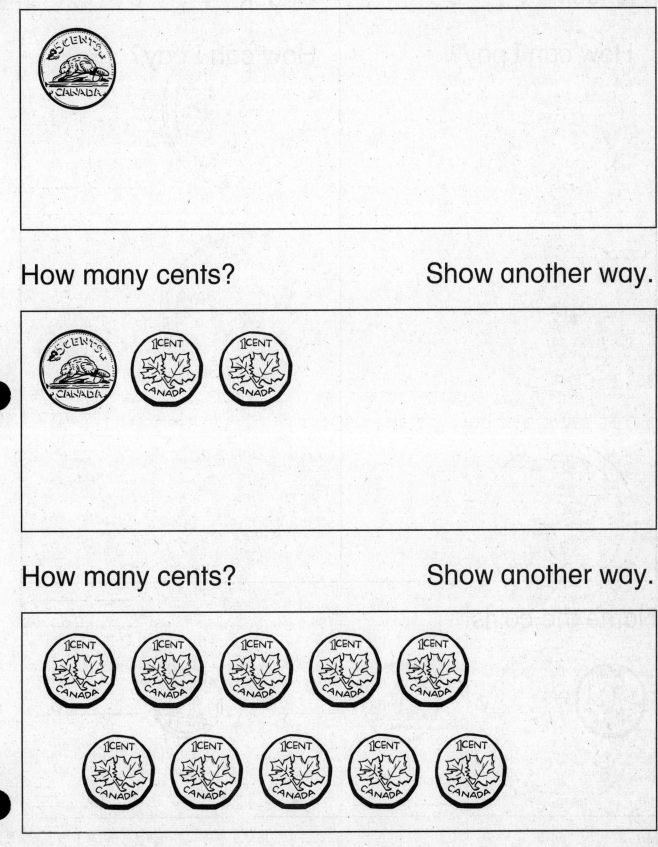

How many cents?　　　　　　　　**Show another way.**

How many cents?　　　　　　　　**Show another way.**

　　　　Chapter 10 Lesson 7　　　　Activity 10.7　　**91**

Counting Coins for Snacks

Snack _____ ¢

How can I pay?

Snack _____ ¢

How can I pay?

Name the coins.

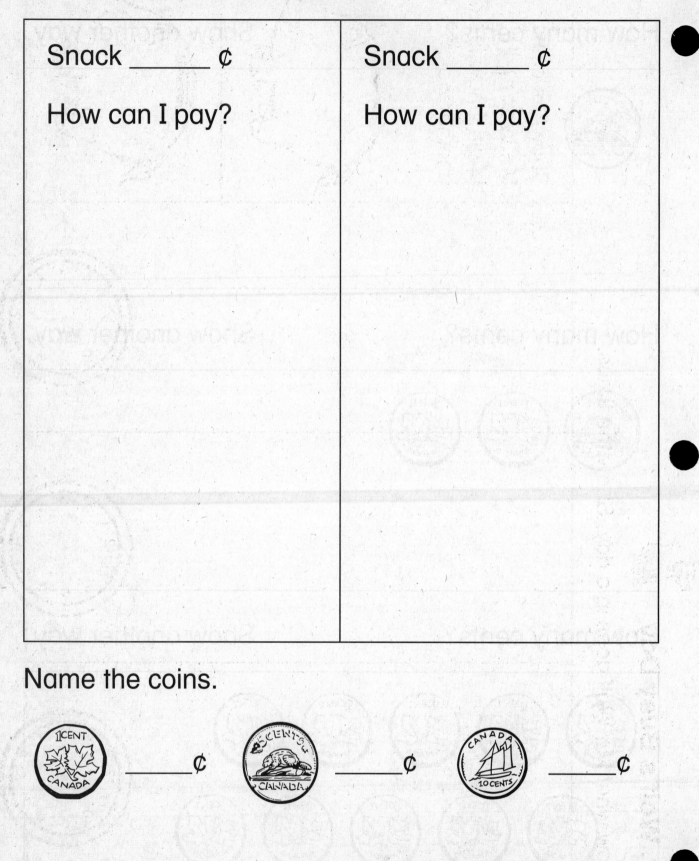

_____ ¢   _____ ¢   _____ ¢

_____ _____ _____

Mr. Wolf's Busy Day

Show what Mr. Wolf does in a day. Show the times.

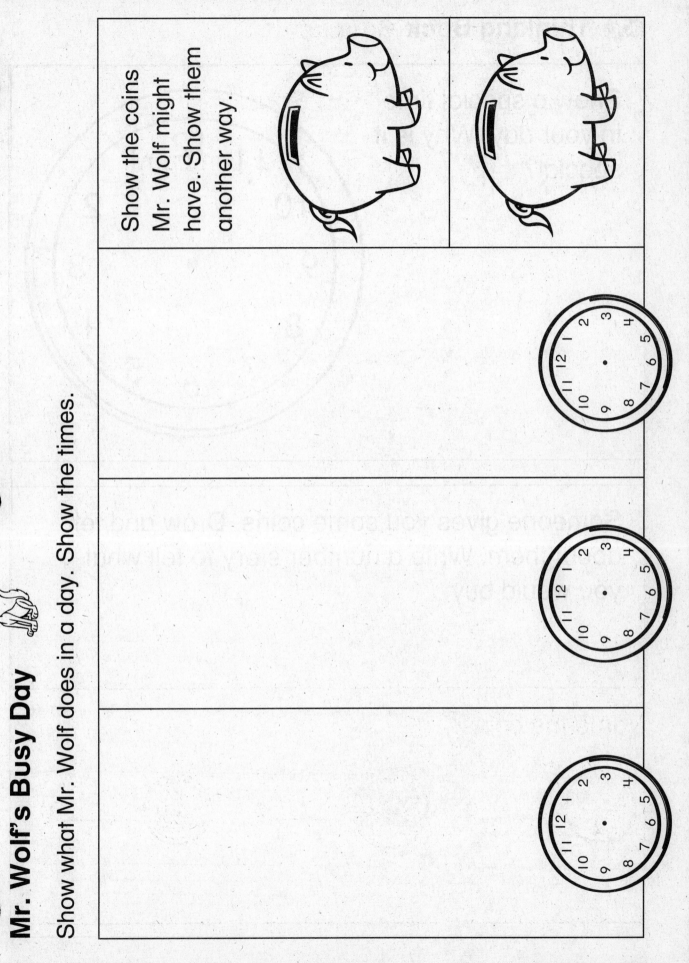

Show the coins Mr. Wolf might have. Show them another way.

Show a special time in your day. Why is it special?

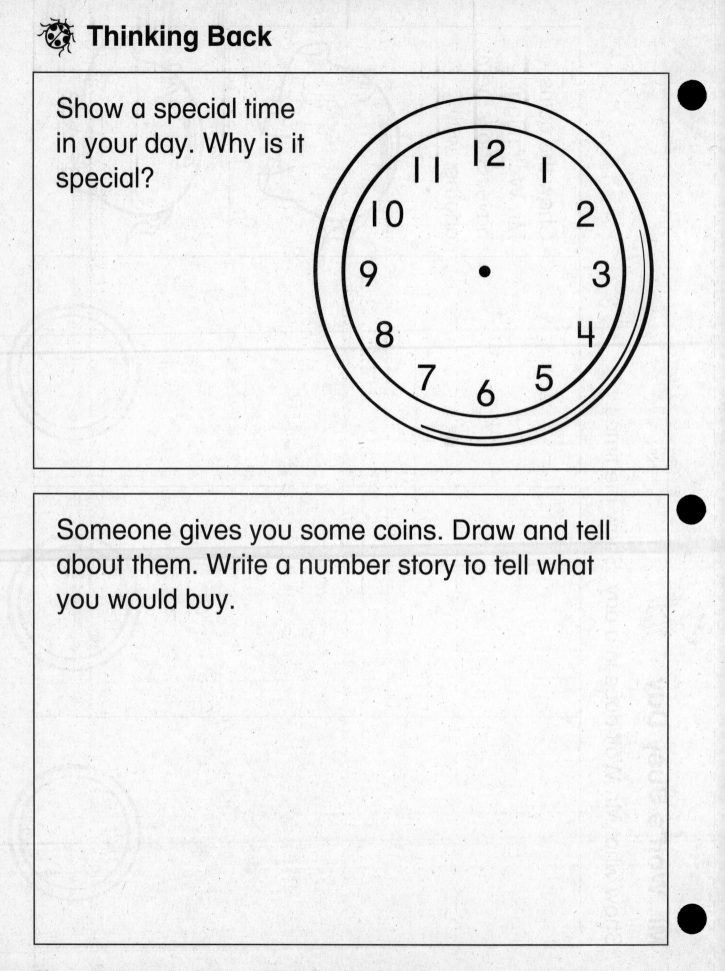

Someone gives you some coins. Draw and tell about them. Write a number story to tell what you would buy.

Chapter 10 Chapter Task

🐞 Write About Math

Describe the train.
Use some of the words you see on the page.

_____

_____

_____

_____

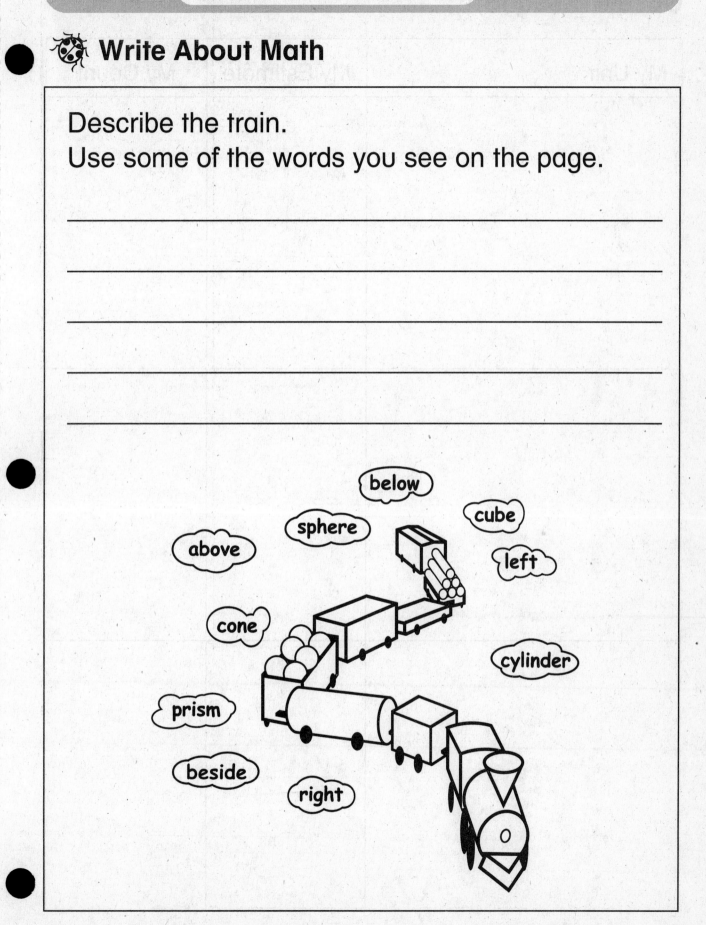

Cover the Square

My Unit	My Estimate	My Count

Glossary Words

area

We can measure the **area** or the amount of space something covers.

We measure area in square units.

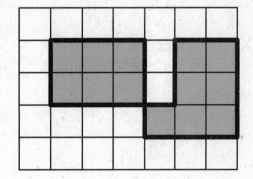

 is 7 square units.

 is _____ square units.

symmetry

These shapes have **symmetry**.

line of symmetry

A shape has symmetry when you can fold it and one part matches the other part.

Circle the letters that have symmetry.

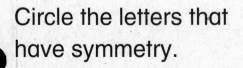

Where Am I?

Draw a picture for each.
Draw yourself in each picture.

Next to me	Above me
Near me	**On my right**

Finish the Shape, Part I

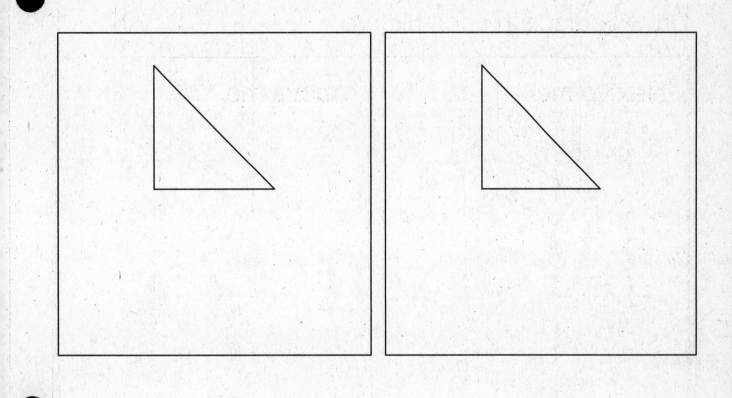

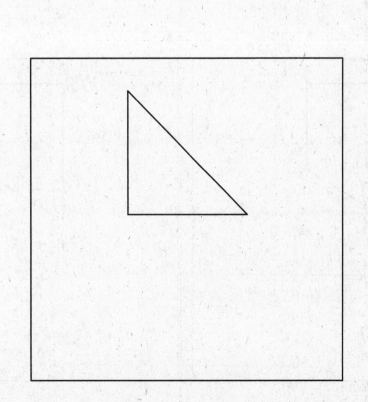

Finish the Shape, Part 2

Chapter 11 Lesson 9

Symmetry Around Me

Draw 4 things you saw that have symmetry.

I also saw these things that have symmetry.

_____   _____

_____   _____

_____   _____

Shape Rules

Make a design. Follow these rules:

- A yellow block must be next to a red one.
- The yellow cannot have the greatest area.
- The design must be symmetrical.

Draw your design here.

Chapter 11 Chapter Task

About My Design

How my design follows the rules:

Two more things about my design:

🐞 Thinking Back

What symmetrical 2-D shapes do you see at home? How would you find the area of one of those shapes?

Write directions for someone to get from your classroom to the library. What things will they pass on the way?

🐞 Write About Math

This is what I know about adding:

This is what I know about subtracting:

Piggy Banks

0 1 2 3 4 5 6 7 8 9 10 11 12 13 14 15 16 17 18

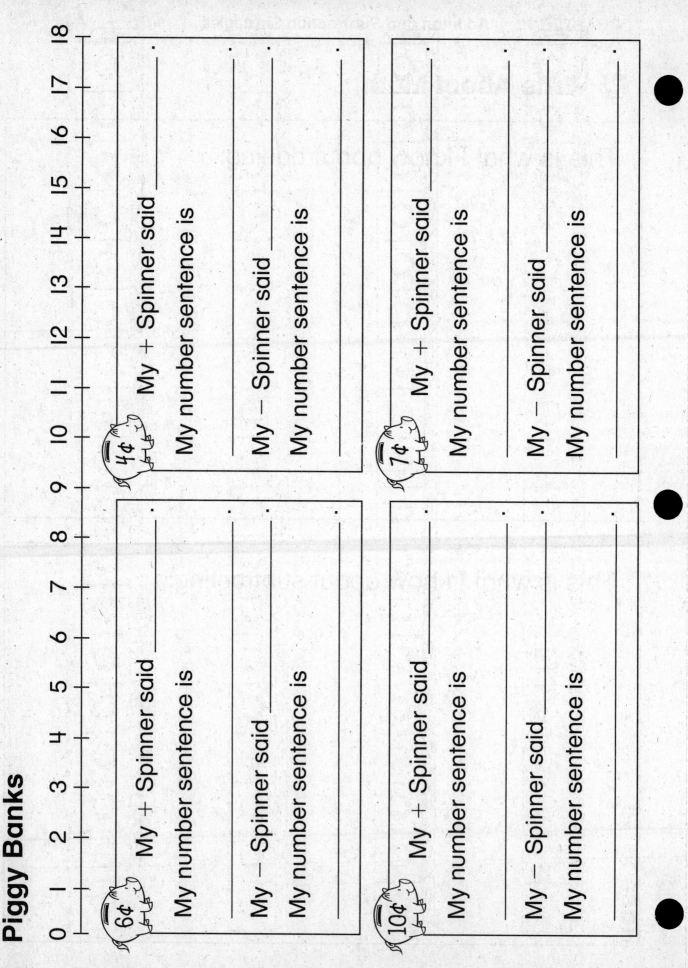

6¢

My + Spinner said _____

My number sentence is _____

My − Spinner said _____

My number sentence is _____

4¢

My + Spinner said _____

My number sentence is _____

My − Spinner said _____

My number sentence is _____

10¢

My + Spinner said _____

My number sentence is _____

My − Spinner said _____

My number sentence is _____

7¢

My + Spinner said _____

My number sentence is _____

My − Spinner said _____

My number sentence is _____

Race to 18

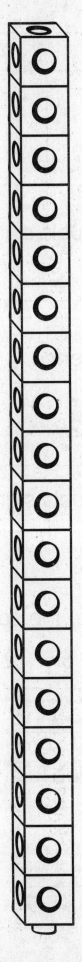

Glossary Words

addition fact

Here are the symbols and words we use to talk about **addition facts**.

Write an addition fact.

$$2 + 3 = 5 \longleftarrow \text{sum}$$

plus sign   equals sign

subtraction fact

Here are the symbols and words we use to talk about **subtraction facts**.

Write a subtraction fact.

difference

$$5 - 3 = 2$$

minus sign   equals sign

doubles fact

A **doubles fact** tells the sum of 2 numbers that are the same.

$$2 + 2 = 4 \qquad 4 + 4 = 8 \qquad 6 + 6 = 12$$

Draw dots to make a doubles fact. Write the doubles fact.

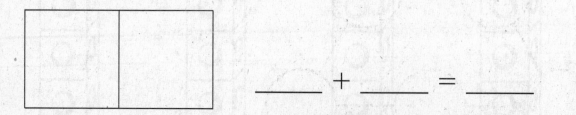

_____ + _____ = _____

Triangle Puzzles

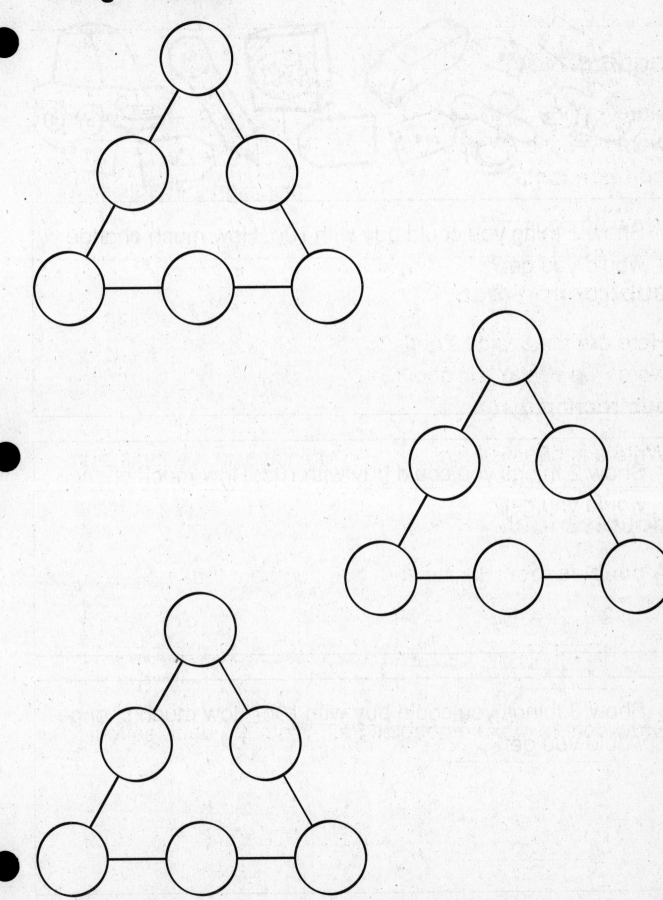

Yard Sale

Show 1 thing you could buy with 10¢. How much change would you get?

Show 2 things you could buy with 10¢. How much change would you get?

Show 3 things you could buy with 10¢. How much change would you get?

How Much Did I Spend?

What did each person buy with 10¢?

Draw a picture.

Finish the number sentence.

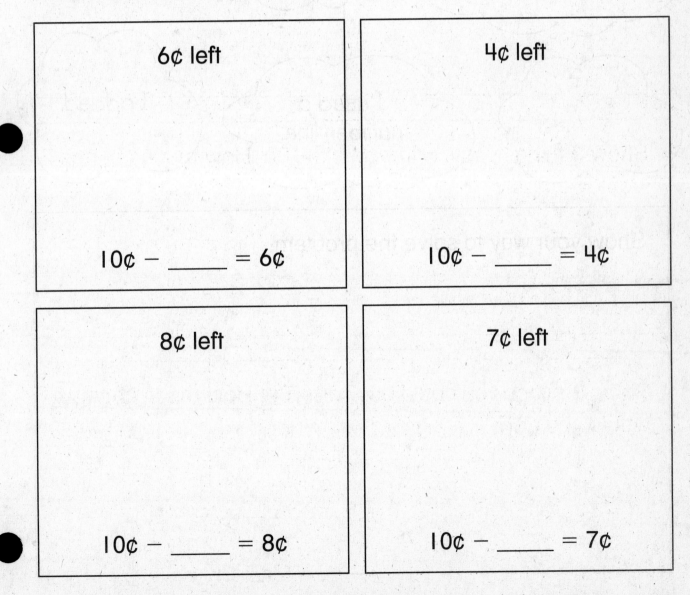

6¢ left	4¢ left
10¢ − _____ = 6¢	10¢ − _____ = 4¢
8¢ left	7¢ left
10¢ − _____ = 8¢	10¢ − _____ = 7¢

I'm a Math Thinker

Colour and write to show the math thinking you used.

I counted up.

I counted back.

I used a number line.

I added.

Show your way to solve the problem.

Using Simpler Facts

7 + 6 = _____

I used these facts: _____

_____ .

I thought:

8 + 4 = _____

I used these facts: _____

_____ .

I thought:

5 + 7 = _____

I used these facts: _____

_____ .

I thought:

9 + 5 = _____

I used these facts: _____

_____ .

I thought:

The Silly Stuff Sale

Kim went to the Silly Stuff sale.

She took 20¢.

She wants to buy

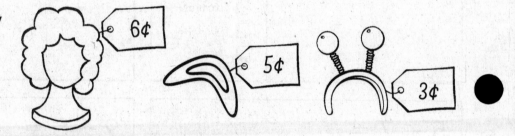

How much money will she have left? _____

What could Kim buy with the money she has left?

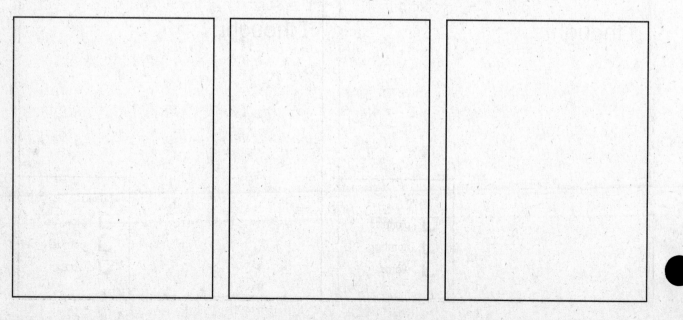

Chapter 12 Chapter Task

Doubles facts are special.

Draw a picture to show some doubles facts.

How can you figure out the sum of 8 + 5?

Draw a picture or use words to show some ways.

🐞 Write About Math

Sometimes I like to

I never like to

Things I Do

● My season is _____.

If it is _____,

then I sometimes _____

_____.

If it is _____,

● then I never _____

_____.

If it is _____,

then I always _____

_____.

● Things I Do

Glossary Words

always, sometimes, never

When you talk about if something might happen, you can use words like: **always**, **sometimes**, **never.**

The sun always sets.

A dog will never fly an airplane.

This spinner will sometimes land on white. It will sometimes land on black.

Colour this spinner so that it always lands on blue.

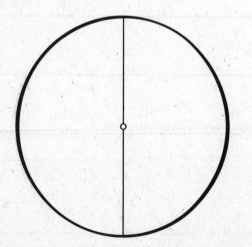

Colour this spinner so that it sometimes lands on red.

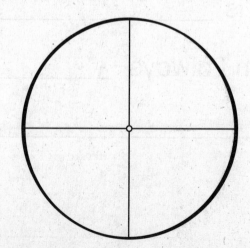

What's in the Bag?

● 1. Take a counter. What colour is it?

Make a tally mark to keep track. Do 10 tries.

_____	_____

2. Colour squares to show the colours you got.

_____

_____

● 3. Use pictures, numbers, or words.

What could be in the bag?	What else could be in the bag?

I'm a Math Thinker

Colour and write to show the math thinking you used.

I made a tally chart.

I made a graph.

I did an experiment.

I predicted.

I compared.

Show how you figured out what was in the bag.

My Survey

1. My survey question was _____

   _____.

2. Here are
   my results.

Always	Sometimes	Never

3. Tell about your survey. Use pictures, numbers, and words.

What I did	What I found out

What's Up?

1. I think it will take _____ tosses to finish the game.

2. Play the game.
   Go left for heads.
   Go right for tails.
   Tally each toss.

Heads	Tails

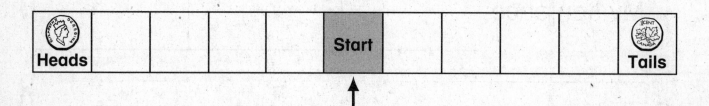

3. What happened when you played?

Always Happened	Sometimes Happened	Never Happened

Chapter 13 Chapter Task

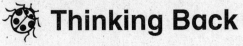 **Thinking Back**

Choose 2 words.

always   sometimes   never

Write 2 sentences. Use one of the words in each sentence.

First word: _____

My sentence:

_____

_____

_____

- -

Second word: _____

My sentence:

_____

_____

_____

Chapter 13 Chapter Task

🐞 Write About Math

Draw a pattern around the page.

What patterns have you seen?

What patterns have you made?

Patterns in the Park

● A pattern I see is:

I made the same pattern this way:

●

The pattern rule is:

●

Toothpick Patterns

Number of shapes	Draw your shape	Number of toothpicks
1		
2		
3		
4		
5		
6		

Chapter 14 Lesson 2

How Does Your Garden Grow?

Number of flowers	Flowers	Number of blocks
1		
2		
3		
4		
5		
6		

How did it grow? What is the pattern?

Chapter 14 Lesson 3

Glossary Words

number patterns

Some **number patterns** repeat.
Show what comes next in this pattern.

\ \|| \|||| \ \|| \||||| \ \|| \||||| \ \|| \||||| _____

Some **number patterns** grow.
Show what comes next in this pattern.

▱▱ ▱▱▱ ▱▱▱▱ ▱▱▱▱▱ _____

odd and even numbers

Numbers are either **even** or **odd**.
Even numbers make pairs.

Some even numbers
are _____.

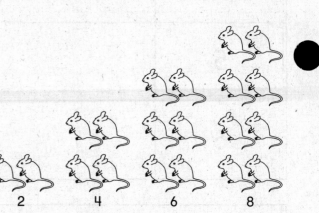

2   4   6   8

Odd numbers do not make
pairs. There is one left over.

Some odd numbers
are _____.

1   3   5   7

Chapter 14 Lessons 3 and 4

How Many Dots?

Number of ladybugs	Number of dots

Show the pattern in the poem.

100 Chart

1	2	3	4	5	6	7	8	9	10
11	12	13	14	15	16	17	18	19	20
21	22	23	24	25	26	27	28	29	30
31	32	33	34	35	36	37	38	39	40
41	42	43	44	45	46	47	48	49	50
51	52	53	54	55	56	57	58	59	60
61	62	63	64	65	66	67	68	69	70
71	72	73	74	75	76	77	78	79	80
81	82	83	84	85	86	87	88	89	90
91	92	93	94	95	96	97	98	99	100

Dogs and Foxes

Draw what you made. How many did you make?

This is how I solved the problem:

Here is another way to solve the problem:

I used

☐ pictures

☐ numbers

☐ words

🐞 Thinking Back

Tell 3 things you have learned about patterns.

1. _____

_____

2. _____

_____

3. _____

_____

Draw or tell how you can use a pattern to help solve a problem or answer a question.

add

Activity 4.3

We **add** to find out how many in all.
Sometimes one group
joins another group.

2 + 1

There are 3 squirrels in all.

Sometimes there are
two groups.

2 + 3

There are 5 animals in all.

addition fact

Activity 12.4

An **addition fact** tells the sum of 2 numbers.

$$2 + 3 = 5 \longleftarrow \text{sum}$$

plus sign   equals sign

addition number sentence

Activity 6.2

We can use numbers and symbols
to tell about **addition**.

We can write $3 + 2 = 5$.
We read it as "three plus two equals five."

$3 + 2 = 5$ ← sum

plus   equals

---

always

Activity 13.3

If something **always** happens, it happens all the time or every
time.

The sun always sets.

---

area

Activity 11.3

We can measure the **area** or the amount of space something
covers. We measure area in square units.

The area is 35 square units.

Glossary

The area is 7 square units.

bar graph

Activity 3.3

We use a **bar graph** to show information. Bars on the graph are different lengths. They show different amounts.

The bar above Spring is tallest. Spring is the favourite season of 9 students in Room 202.

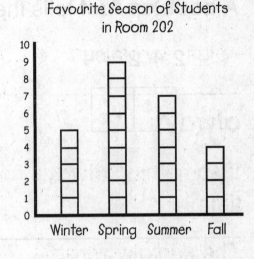

Favourite Season of Students in Room 202

capacity

Activity 9.2

Capacity means how much something holds.
We fill things to find out how much they can hold.

It's not full.

It's full.

holds more   holds less

Glossary

dime

Activity 8.3

A **dime** is a coin worth 10¢.

doubles fact

Activity 12.4

A **doubles fact** tells the sum of 2 numbers that are the same.

$$2 + 2 = 4 \qquad 4 + 4 = 8 \qquad 6 + 6 = 12$$

even numbers

Activity 14.5

Numbers are either **even** or **odd**.

Even numbers make pairs.

2   4   6   8

Glossary

graph

Activity 3.3

● We use **graphs** to show information and put it in order.

Some graphs use real objects.
Some graphs use pictures of objects.
Some graphs use symbols.
Graphs have titles and labels.

Sink or Float?

Sink   Float

---

half

Activity 9.7

2 equal parts of a whole are called **halves**. Each of the parts is one **half**.

●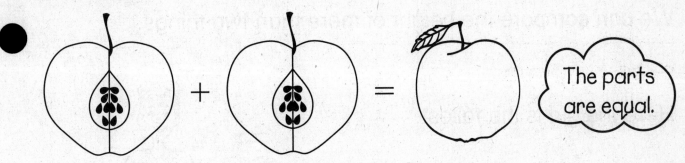

The parts are equal.

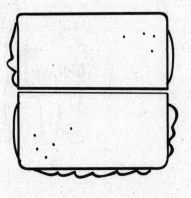

height

We can measure to compare **height**.

The mouse is **shorter** than the giraffe.

The giraffe is **taller** than the mouse.

We can compare the height of more than two things.

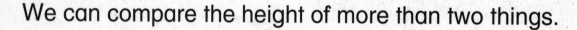

Here the girl is the tallest.

The baby is the shortest.

hour

Activity 10.5

There are 24 **hours** in one **day**.
There are 60 **minutes** in one **hour**.

We use a **clock** to measure time.
This clock has the numbers 1 to 12.
It has a **minute hand** and an **hour hand**.

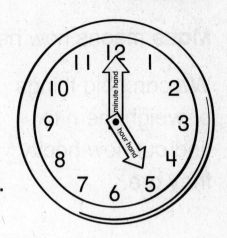

length

Activity 5.3

We can measure to compare the **length** of two things.

The pen is longer than the chalk.
The chalk is shorter than the pen.

longer

shorter

We can compare the **length** of more than two things.

The pencil is the longest thing.
The crayon is the shortest thing.

longest

shortest

Glossary

mass

Mass means how heavy something is.

We can hold things or weigh them to find out how heavy they are.

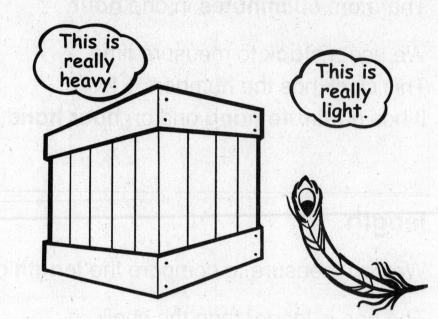

We can use a **balance** to compare how heavy things are.

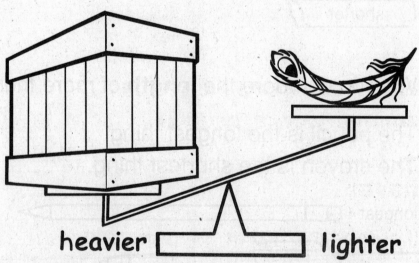

Glossary

money

We use **money** to buy things.
Here are the **coins** we can use.

	penny	1¢
	nickel	5¢
	dime	10¢
	quarter	25¢

month

There are 12 **months** in one **year**.
A calendar helps to measure time.
A calendar shows the year in
months, **weeks**, and **days**.

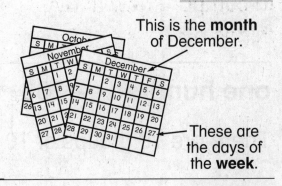

This is the **month** of December.

These are the days of the **week**.

never

If something **never** happens, it does not ever happen.

A dog will never fly an airplane.

number patterns

Some **number patterns** repeat.

\ \ / //// \ \ / //// \ \ / //// \ \ / ////

1 3 6   1 3 6   1 3 6   1 3 6

Some **number patterns** grow.

2   4   6   8

odd numbers

Numbers are either **even** or **odd**.

Odd numbers do not make pairs.
There is one left over.

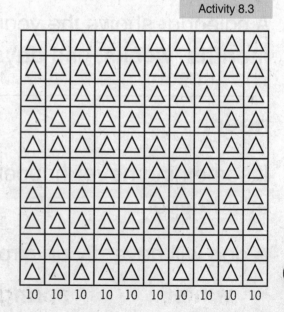

1   3   5   7

one hundred — 100

There are 10 groups of 10 in **100**.

10 10 10 10 10 10 10 10 10 10

Glossary

pattern

A **pattern** is something that happens over and over again.

happy face   heart   happy face   heart   happy face   heart

circle   circle   square   circle   circle   square   circle   circle   square

picture graph

We use a **picture graph** to show information.

The most pictures are above vanilla.
Vanilla is the favourite ice cream flavour of 5 students in Room 202.

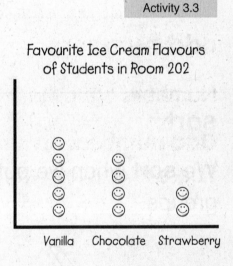

Favourite Ice Cream Flavours of Students in Room 202

Vanilla   Chocolate   Strawberry

season

There are four **seasons** in a year.
The seasons are **winter**, **spring**, **summer**, **fall**.

winter   **spring**   **summer**   **fall**

sometimes

If something **sometimes** happens it happens now and then.

This spinner will sometimes land on white. It will sometimes land on black.

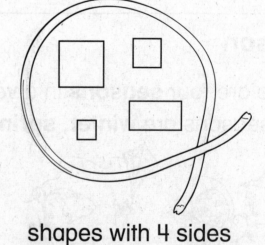

---

sort

We **sort** when we put things that are alike in some way in groups.

shapes with 3 sides   shapes with 4 sides

Glossary   Copyright © 2004 Nelson Education Ltd.

subtract

We **subtract** to find out
how many are left.

$4 - 2$
There are 2 birds left in
the nest.

We also **subtract** to compare numbers.

Sometimes we **subtract** to find
the missing number or parts.

$5 - 1 = 4$
1 ball is missing.

5 balls

subtraction fact

A **subtraction fact** tells the difference between 2 numbers.

$$5 - 3 = 2 \longleftarrow \text{difference}$$

minus sign   equals sign

subtraction number sentence

We can use numbers and symbols to tell about **subtraction**.

We can write $6 - 2 = 4$.

We read it as "six minus two equals four."

$6 - 2 = 4$ ← difference

↑ minus ↑ equals

---

symmetry

These shapes have **symmetry**.

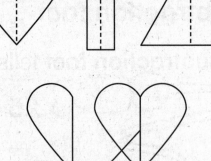

A shape has **symmetry** when you can fold it and one part matches the other part.

line of symmetry

Glossary

ten — 10

● **10** is the number that comes after 9.

10 is the number that comes before 11.

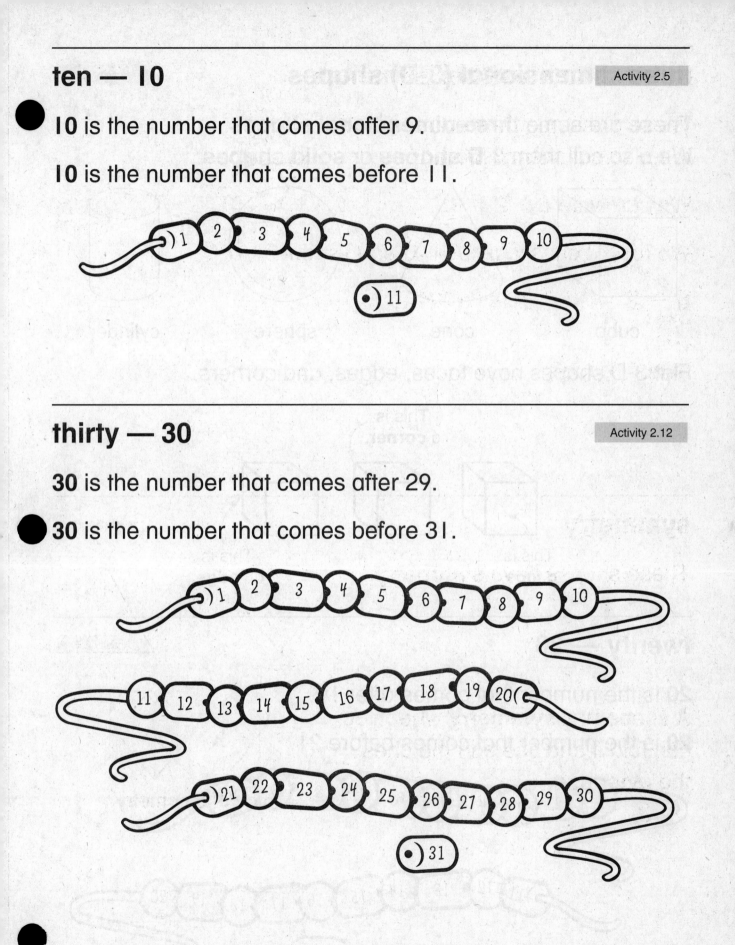

---

thirty — 30

30 is the number that comes after 29.

● **30** is the number that comes before 31.

three-dimensional (3-D) shapes

These are some **three-dimensional shapes**.
We also call them **3-D shapes** or **solid shapes**.

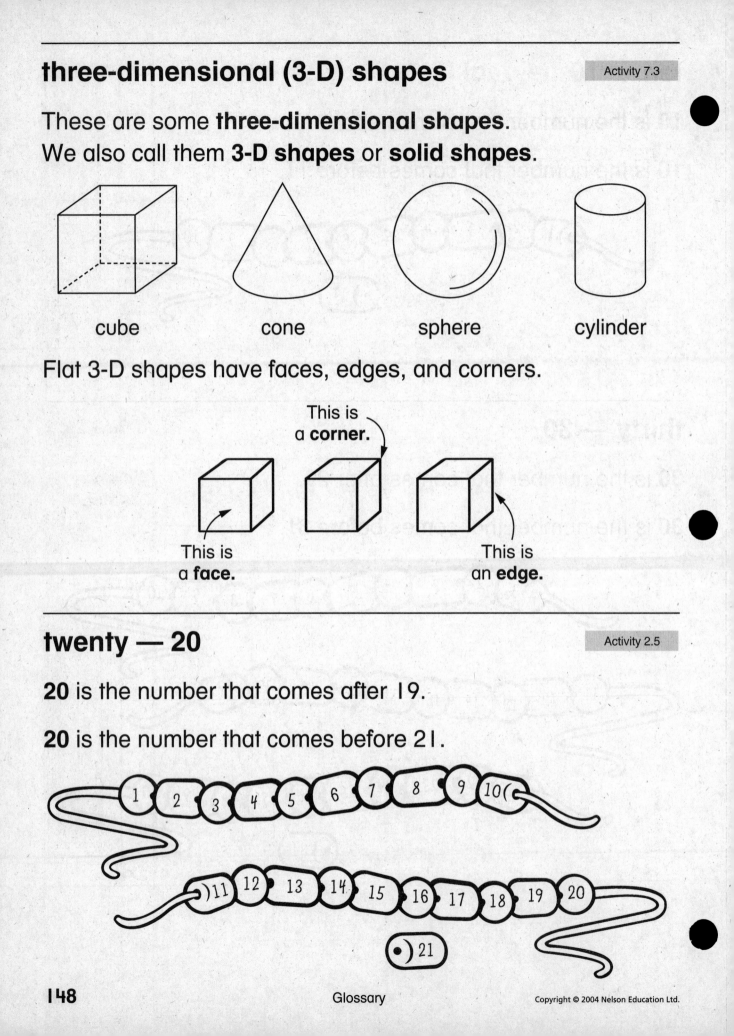

cube   cone   sphere   cylinder

Flat 3-D shapes have faces, edges, and corners.

This is
a **corner.**

This is
a **face.**

This is
an **edge.**

---

twenty — 20

20 is the number that comes after 19.

20 is the number that comes before 21.

Glossary

two-dimensional (2-D) shapes

These are some **two-dimensional shapes**.
When a shape is flat we call it a two-dimensional shape.

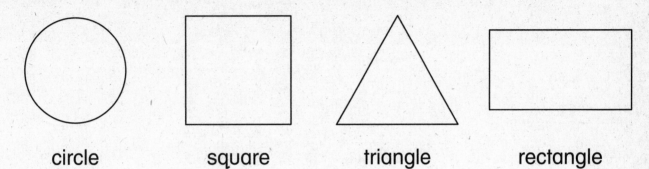

circle   square   triangle   rectangle

Flat 2-D shapes have sides and corners.

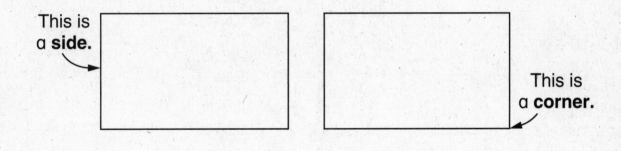

This is
a **side.**

This is
a **corner.**

Glossary   **149**